The sensory world of the autistic spectrum: a greater understanding

Kate Wilkes
NAS Autism Helpline

Contents

Introduction   1
   Sensory integration   2
   Balance   2
   Body awareness   2
   Smell   3
   Sight   3
   Hearing   4
   Touch   4
   Taste   5
   Additional sensory difficulties   5
Possible strategies   6
   General points to remember   6
   Sensory Integration Therapy   6
   Balance ideas   6
   Body awareness ideas   7
   Smell ideas   7
   Sight ideas   7
   Hearing ideas   8
   Touch ideas   9
   Sensory rooms   9
Appendix 1 Professionals who can help   10
Appendix 2 Sensory problems and coping strategies   11
References   12
Useful contacts   13
Recommended reading   15

Introduction

Many people on the autistic spectrum experience sensory difficulties or are particularly sensitive to certain sensations. These difficulties may result in behaviour which parents and carers find puzzling.

This booklet aims to give a basic understanding of sensory integration, explain possible difficulties individuals on the spectrum may have and offer strategies to help. It aims to provide people with an awareness of the sensory world of individuals with autism.

Throughout this booklet the term autism is used to include autistic spectrum disorders (ASD), autism and Asperger syndrome.

To function and participate in the world that surrounds us, we need to use our senses. Senses provide individuals with unique experiences and allow us to interact and be involved with the rest of society. They help us to understand the environment around us and respond within it. They play a significant role in determining what actions we take within a particular situation.

Imagine what happens when just one or all of the senses are intensified or are not present at all. This difficulty is often called sensory integration dysfunction and it is one that many individuals on the autistic spectrum experience.

There are several definitions of autism but they rarely state what an individual with autism feels. We can only get an insight through personal accounts of individuals with autism who can express and describe their unique and often painful sensory world.

Everyday experiences which the majority of non-autistic individuals take for granted can for autistic individuals be negative and upsetting experiences. Behaviours presented by someone with autism will often be a direct reaction to their sensory experience.

It is therefore understandable why individuals with autism create rituals or have self-stimulatory behaviours such as spinning, flapping and tapping, because these make them feel that they are in control and feel safe in their unique world.

'If I get sensory overload then I just shut down... you get what's known as fragmentation... it's weird, like being tuned into 40 TV channels.' [1]

1

Sensory integration

Dr A. Jean Ayres defines sensory integration as 'the organisation of sensation for use.' [2] Sensory integration involves turning sensation into perception.

The central nervous system (brain) processes all the sensory information sent from various sensory systems in the body and helps to organise, prioritise and understand the information. From this it is able to action a response – thoughts, feelings, motor responses (behaviour) or a combination of these.

Throughout our bodies we have receptors, which pick up on sensory stimuli. Our hands and feet contain the most receptors. Most of the time the processing of sensory information is automatic.

The sensory systems can be broken down into six areas. These can be divided into two main areas hyper (high) and hypo (low) sensitivity. However, it is important to remember that the difficulties/differences may for some individuals fall into both areas.

This section makes extensive use of Brenda Smith Myles' excellent explanations on sensory integration in the following notes. For further details please see her book. [3]

Balance (vestibular) system

Situated in the inner ear, this provides us with information on where our body is in space and its speed, direction and movement, all in relation to the pull of gravity. It is fundamental in helping us to keep our balance and posture. For an individual on the autistic spectrum, difficulties/differences may be:

Hypo

- the need for rocking, swinging, spinning.

Hyper

- difficulties in activities which include movement – sport
- difficulties in stopping quickly or during an activity.

Body awareness (proprioception) system

Situated in the muscles and joints, this tells us where our bodies are. It also informs us where our body parts are and how they are moving. For an individual on the autistic spectrum difficulties/differences may be:

Hypo

- proximity – standing too close to others
- lack of awareness of personal body space
- difficulties in navigating rooms – avoiding obstructions
- bumping into people.

Hyper

- difficulties with fine motor skills, manipulating small objects (buttons, tying shoe laces)
- movement of the whole body to look at something.

Smell (olfactory) system

By processing through chemical receptors in the nose, this tells us about smells in our immediate environment. Smell is a sense that is often neglected and forgotten about. It is, however, the first sense we rely upon. For an individual on the spectrum difficulties/differences may be:

Hypo

- some individuals have no sense of smell and fail to notice extreme odours
- individuals may lick objects.

Hyper

- smells can be intensified and become overpowering
- toileting problems
- dislike of individuals with distinctive perfumes, shampoos.

'Smells like dogs, cats, deodorant and after shave lotion are so strong to me I can't stand it, and perfume drives me nuts.' [4]

Sight (visual) system

Situated in the retina of the eye and activated by light, our sight helps us to define objects, people, colours, contrast and spatial boundaries. For an individual on the autistic spectrum, possible difficulties/differences include:

Hypo

- may see things darker and lose features or lines
- some may concentrate on peripheral vision because their central vision is blurred. Others say that a main object is magnified and things on the periphery become blurred
- poor depth perception – problems with throwing and catching; clumsiness.

Hyper

- distorted vision occurs
- small objects and bright lights can jump around
- fragmentation of images as a consequence of too many sources
- focusing on particular details such as sand grains may be more pleasurable than looking at something as a whole.

'She was Mrs Marek, a face upon which light danced maniacally, turning her into more of a cartoon than a human being. Welcome to Toon town... I'd like you to enter this torture chamber I call my kitchen and meet my wife who is a 3D cartoon.' [5]

Hearing (auditory) system

Situated in the inner ear, this informs us about sounds in the environment. It is the most commonly recognised aspect of sensory impairment. For an individual on the autistic spectrum, difficulties/differences may be:

Hypo

- sounds may only be heard with one ear, with the other ear either only having partial hearing or none at all
- the person may not acknowledge particular sounds
- may enjoy crowded noisy places, kitchens, bangs doors and objects.

Hyper

- volume of noise can be magnified and surrounding sounds distorted and muddled
- inability to cut out particular sounds, leading to difficulties concentrating
- may have a lower hearing threshold, which makes them particularly sensitive to auditory stimuli, for example hearing conversations in the distance.

Hearing impairment can have a direct effect on the ability to communicate and may also affect their balance.

'Do you hear noise in your head? It pounds and screeches. Like a train rumbling through your ears.' [6]

Touch (tactile) system

Situated on the skin, the body's largest organ, this relates to touch, type of pressure and level of pain and helps us distinguish temperature (hot and cold).

Touch is a significant component in social development. It helps us to assess the environment we are in and enables us to react accordingly. For an individual on the autistic spectrum difficulties/differences may be:

Hypo

- holds others tightly
- has high pain or temperature threshold
- self harming
- may enjoy heavy objects on top of them.

Hyper

- touch can be painful and uncomfortable and they will often withdraw from aspects of touch, which can have a grave effect on their relationships with others
- dislike of having anything on hands or feet
- difficulties in brushing and washing hair
- only likes certain types of clothing, textures.

'Every time I am touched it hurts – it feels like fire running through my body.' [7]

Taste (gustatory) system

Processed through chemical receptors in the tongue, this tells us about different tastes – sweet, sour, bitter, salty and spicy. Individuals will often have restricted diets as a result of their taste buds being extra sensitive. For an individual on the spectrum difficulties/differences may be:

Hypo

- likes very spicy foods
- pica: eats everything – soil, grass, materials.

Hyper

- some flavours and foods are too strong and over-powering for them
- certain textures may cause discomfort. Some children will only eat smooth foods such as mashed potatoes or ice cream.

Additional sensory difficulties

Synathesia

This is a rare condition, separate from ASD, which some individuals on the spectrum say they experience. This is when confusion in the sensory channels occurs. A sensory experience goes in through one system and out through a different system. For example an individual hears a sound (auditory system) but sees colours (visual system).

Possible strategies

A greater understanding of the sensory world of individuals on the spectrum allows you to help them develop in a more comfortable environment.

The following strategies may help when trying to create a comfortable environment for an individual on the autistic spectrum to avoid their senses being overloaded.

General points to remember

Awareness

Remember that sensory dysfunction may be the reason for the problem and always examine the environment.

Be creative

Use your imagination to come up with positive sensory experiences and/or strategies.

Prepare

Always warn the individual of possible sensory stimuli they may experience – e.g. loud crowded places.

Sensory Integration Therapy

Sensory Integration Therapy involves gentle exposure to various sensory stimuli. The aim of this therapy is to strengthen, balance and develop the central nervous system's processing of sensory stimuli.

Carl Delacato, who developed the concept of Sensory Integration Therapy, focused the therapy on the five core sensory systems - vision, taste, smell, hearing and touch. Today, Occupational Therapists continue to focus on these areas, as well as incorporating the vestibular and proprioception systems, when creating and planning a schedule of activities for an individual.

Balance (vestibular) ideas

Hypo

- encourage activities which help develop the vestibular system, such as rocking horse, swing, roundabout and seesaws.

Hyper

- break down activities into small steps, use visual clues such as a finish line or prompts.

Body awareness (propriocepition) ideas

Hypo

- position furniture around the edge of the room to make navigation easier
- put coloured tape on the floor to indicate boundaries
- use the arm's length rule to help with personal body space. When talking to people, hold out your arm to check you are not standing too close. Remember to put your arm down when you are talking.

Hyper

- threading activities, such as threading string through cotton reels or lace boards. Both develop fine motor movements.

Smell (olfactory) ideas

Hypo

- use strong smelling products as rewards and to distract from possibly inappropriate strong smelling stimuli, eg faeces.

Hyper

- use unscented detergents or shampoos, refrain from wearing perfumes, make the environment as fragrance-free as possible.

Sight (visual) ideas

Irlen lenses/orthoscoptics

These methods are very similar and refer to perceptual processing difficulties in relation to the visual system. By using coloured overlays and tinted lenses, the aim is to improve and reduce environmental distortions, print distortions and sensory overload. A questionnaire is used to screen and identify specific difficulties and to establish the correct lenses for the individual. For further information see contacts/recommended reading.

Hyper

- reduce fluorescent lighting by using deep coloured light bulbs instead
- sunglasses
- use blackout curtains
- create a workstation in the classroom: a space or desk with high walls or divides on both sides to block out visual distractions from the front and sides.

Hearing (auditory) ideas

Auditory Integration Training (A.I.T.)

This is based on the theory that behaviours are a consequence of difficulties in the auditory system.

In the early 1980's Dr Guy Berard created a machine to test and exercise the individual's auditory system. By producing and altering various sounds the machine is able to use auditory filters to maximize the volume without causing discomfort. The aim is to train the auditory system and balance its input. Research into this approach is very limited. For further information see contacts/recommended reading below.

Music therapy

The benefits of music therapy have been recognised, and it is often used with individuals on the autistic spectrum. Music therapy provides individuals with a unique opportunity to communicate, interact and express themselves. For further information see contacts/recommended reading below.

Hyper

- shut doors and windows to reduce external noise
- prepare the individual before going to a noisy place or crowded situations.
- ear plugs
- personal stereo
- create a work station – see above for help on how to do this.

Touch (tactile) ideas

Hypo

- weighted blankets
- sleeping bags.

Hyper

- warn the child if you are about to touch him. Always try to approach from the front.
- remember - a hug may be painful rather than comforting!
- gradually introduce different textures – have a box of materials available
- allow the individual to complete activities such as hair brushing and washing themselves, enabling them to regulate their sensitivity.

Sensory rooms

Sensory rooms or multi sensory environments (MSE) aim to offer individuals with autism the opportunity to stimulate, develop or balance their sensory systems.

They are located mainly in specialist schools or hospitals so access is quite limited. However, many families have chosen to adapt a room in their home to create a space for sensory stimulation or reload.

Hulsegge and Verheul[8] developed the concept of the sensory room in the Netherlands, drawing from the work of Clark[8] who established the idea of 'SNOEZLEN' rooms. The name is a combination of two words: to 'smell' and to 'dose'. The terms more commonly used in the UK are sensory rooms or multi sensory environments.

Rooms or sensory spaces can take various forms or focus on different types of sensation. They may be white or dark rooms, contain different sounds or allow for interactive play. Water or softplay resources may be used. Sensory gardens appeal to the sense of smell, sight or touch. The main functions of MSE are therapeutic, educational and relaxation, all in relation to development.

Equipment used within the rooms varies depending on the type, function and needs of the individual using it. The following list gives examples of equipment to provide stimulation for all sensory systems.

Stimuli can include soothing music, vibrating cushions, fibre optics, mirror balls, bubble tubes, waterbeds, tactile walls, disco lights and projectors, to name just a few. The MSE can be set up with switches, pressure, sound and movement to activate a piece of equipment in the room. The child learns to recognise cause and effect.

Benefits of MSE at present rely mainly upon personal experiences and observations, as there is only a limited amount of research.

Appendix 1
Professionals who can help

Occupational therapists (OT) – play a vital role in sensory difficulties by designing programmes and often making adaptations to environments to ensure individuals are able to live as independently as possible.

Sensory impairment teams – accessed through local social and health services, these teams specialise in sensory difficulties. Although they are not autism specific, some local authorities do cover individuals on the autistic spectrum.

Speech and language therapists – often use sensory stimuli to encourage and support the development of language and interaction.

Music therapists – use instruments and sounds (auditory stimuli) to encourage and develop the sensory systems, predominately the auditory system.

Appendix 2
Sensory problems and coping strategies

Problem	possible sensory reasons	ideas
Picky eater	sensitive to taste or texture, maybe unable to feel the food around mouth	slowly introduce different textures around the individual's mouth – flannel, toothbrush, foods, introduce small portions, change texture of the food, puree it. Encourage activities that involve the mouth – whistles, bubble wands, straw painting
Chews on everything – clothing and objects	may find this relaxing, enjoys the tactile input of the item	latex free tubes, straws, hard gums (chill in fridge)
Smearing	may like the texture in their hands or be hypo-sensitive to smells	try and introduce similar materials – jelly, cornflour and water.
Refuses to wear certain clothes	may dislike the texture, pressure on their skin	turn items inside out – so there is no seam, remove any tags or labels, allow them to wear clothes that they are comfortable in.
Difficulties getting to sleep	may have difficulty shutting down senses, in particular visual and auditory	use blackout curtains, allow child to listen to music to cut out external sounds, weighted blankets.
Finds concentrating in the classroom difficult	may have too many sensory distractions – too noisy (talking, bells, chairs scraping the floor), lots of visual stimuli (people, pictures on the wall), may also find holding a pencil uncomfortable (hard/cold)	Position them away from the doors and windows, use furniture in the room to create an area free from distraction or if possible an individual workstation, try different textures to make the pencil more comfortable.

References

[1] Personal comment to author by a client with autism

[2] Ayres, A.J. (1979) *Sensory integration and the child*, Los Angeles, Western Psychological Services

[3] Smith Myles, B., Tapscott Cook, K., Miller, N.E , Rinner, L., Robbins, L. A (2000) *Asperger Syndrome and sensory issues – practical solutions for making sense of the world*, Shawnee Mission, Kansas, Autism Asperger Publishing Co

[4] Gillingham G. (1995) *Autism: handle with care! Understanding and managing behavior of children and adults with autism*, Arlington, Texas, Future Education Inc, p60

[5] Gillingham G. (1995) *Autism: handle with care! Understanding and managing behavior of children and adults with autism*, Arlington, Texas, Future Education Inc, p51

[6] Gillingham G. (1995) *Autism: handle with care! Understanding and managing behavior of children and adults with autism*, Arlington, Texas, Future Education Inc, p41

[7] Gillingham G. (1995) *Autism: handle with care! Understanding and managing behavior of children and adults with autism*, Arlington, Texas, Future Education Inc, p3

[8] Pagliano, P (2000) *Multisensory environments*, London, David Fulton Ltd

Useful contacts

Equipment suppliers

Nottingham Rehab Supplies
Findel House
Excelsior Road
Ashby Park
Leicestershire
LE65 1NG
Tel: 0845 120 4522
Occupational Therapy Product advisory
helpline: 01530 418 222
Email: info@nrs-uk.co.uk
www.nrs-uk.co.uk

The Sensory Company International Ltd
Broad Lane Business Centre
Westfield Lane
South Elmsall
Pontefract
WF9 2JX
Tel: 01977 646 414
Fax: 01977 646 416
Email: sue.batty@thesensorycompany.co.uk
www.thesensorycompany.co.uk

ROMPA®
Goyt Side Road
Chesterfield
Derbyshire
S40 2PH
Tel: 01246 211 777
www.rompa.com

Winslow
Goyt Side Road
Chesterfield
Derbyshire
S40 2PH
Tel: 0845 230 2777
www.winslow-cat.com

Professionals (C header)
National College of Occupational Therapists
106-114 Borough High Street
London SE1 1LB
Tel: 020 7357 6480
www.cot.org.uk

Occupational Therapists in Independent Practice
18 Woodland Way
Devizes
Wilts SN10 5LA
Tel: 0800 389 4873/01380 720 181
www.otipp.co.uk

Association of Professional Music
Therapists (UK)
26 Hamlyn Road
Glastonbury
Somerset
BA6 8HT
Tel: 01458 834 919

The professional body for qualified music
therapists in the UK. Can advise on music
therapy courses, and put clients in touch with
therapists.

British Society for Music Therapy
25 Rosslyn Avenue
East Barnet
Herts,
EN4 8DH
Tel: 020 8441 6226
Fax: 020 8441 4118
www.bsmt.org

Promotes the use and development of music
therapy. Publishes journals, monographs and
videos, organises conferences and meetings.

Sensory Integration Network
26 Leopardstown Grove
Blackrock
Dublin
Ireland
Email: info@sensoryintegration.org.uk
www.sensoryintegration.org.uk

The National Light and Sound Therapy Centre
(A.I.T.)
80 Queen Elizabeth's Walk
London N16 5UQ
England
Tel: 020 8880 1269
www.light-and-sound.co.uk/

The Delacato Centre
Principal facility: 26 Gwscwm Park
Burry Port
Llanelli
Carmarthenshire SA16 0DX
Tel: 01554 83 69 60
www.delacato.co.uk

Irlen Institute
Irlen Centre East
4 Park Farm Business Centre
Fornham St Genevieve
Bury St Edwards
Suffolk IP28 6TS
Tel: 01284 724 301
www.irlen.com

Orthoscopics Ltd
City Opticians
75-76 Chancery Lane
London
WC2A 1AA
Tel: 020 7405 4875
Email: info@orthoscopics.com
www.orthoscopics.com
www.visualdyslexia.com

Recommended reading

*Attwood, T. (1998) *Asperger's Syndrome – A guide for parents and professionals*, London, Jessica Kingsley Publishers

*Bogdashina, O. (2003) *Sensory Perceptual issues in Autism and Asperger Syndrome – Different sensory Experiences. Different Perceptual Worlds*, London, Jessica Kingsley Publishersers

Delacato. C. H. (1974) *The Ultimate Stranger - the Autistic Child*, USA, Arena Press

*Gerland, G. (1997) A *Real Person – Life on the Outside*, London, Souvenir Press

Gillingham G. (1995) Autism : *handle with care! Understanding and managing behavior of children and adults with autism*, Arlington, Texas, Future Education Inc

*Grandin, T. and Scariano, M. (1986) *Emergence labelled autistic*, New York, Warner

*Grandin, T. (1995) *Thinking in pictures and other reports from my life with autism*, New York, Vintage Books

*Jackson, L. (2002) *Freaks, geeks and Asperger Syndrome*, London, Jessica Kingsley Publishers

*Legge, B. (2001) *Can't eat, won't eat: dietary difficulties and autistic spectrum disorders*, London, Jessica Kingsley Publishers

**National Autistic Society – *Auditory Integration Training fact sheet*

**National Autistic Society – *Music therapy fact sheet*

**National Autistic Society – *Speech and language therapy fact sheet*

Pagliano, P. (2000) *Multisensory environments*, London, David Fulton Publishers

*Smith Myles, B., Tapscott Cook, K., Miller, N.E, Rinner, L., Robbins, L. A (2000) *Asperger syndrome and sensory issues – practical solutions for making sense of the world*, Shawnee Mission, Kansas, Autism Asperger Publishing Co

Williams, D. (1998) *Somebody somewhere*, London, Jessica Kingsley Publishers

Williams, D (1996) *An inside out approach*, London, Jessica Kingsley Publishers

*These books are available from The National Autistic Society publications catalogue
Tel: 020 7903 3595
Email: publications@nas.org.uk
www.autism.org.uk/pubs to order on line and for the full catalogue

**These fact sheets are available from The National Autistic Society Information Centre or on the NAS website
Tel: 020 7903 3599
Email: info@nas.org.uk
www.autism.org.uk/infosheets

The author, Kate Wilkes, works on the NAS Autism Helpline

Many people on the autistic spectrum experience sensory difficulties or are particularly sensitive to certain sensations.

These difficulties may result in behaviour which parents and carers find puzzling.

This booklet aims to
- give a basic understanding of sensory integration
- explain possible difficulties that people individuals with autism or Asperger syndrome may have
- offer coping strategies.

The author, Kate Wilkes, works on the NAS Autism Helpline.

The National Autistic Society
Head Office
393 City Road, London EC1V 1NG
Tel: 020 7833 2299
Fax: 020 7833 9666
nas@nas.org.uk
www.autism.org.uk

Advocacy for Education Service:
0845 070 4002

Autism Helpline: 0845 070 4004
Minicom: 0845 070 4003
(Mon-Fri 10am-4pm)
Email: autismhelpline@nas.org.uk

Information: 0845 070 4004
(Mon-Fri 10am-4pm)
Email: info@nas.org.uk

Membership: 020 7903 3563
Email: membership@nas.org.uk

Publications: 020 7903 3595
Email: publications@nas.org.uk
www.autism.org.uk/pubs

Training: 0115 911 3363
Email: training@nas.org.uk

ISBN 1-899280-58-8

9 781899 280582

Code NAS 552
© The National Autistic Society 2004

The National
Autistic Society

The National Autistic Society is a company limited by guarantee. Registered in England No 1205298. Registered Office: 393 City Road, London, EC1V 1NG. Registered as a Charity No 269425.

The Chiropractor's Femme Fatale

By

John Rees

Dedication

This book is dedicated to my late father, Jack, a just, honourable man of immense integrity, whose love and dedication towards me were never fully appreciated until it was too late to tell him how proud I was to be known as his son. I so hope that history does not repeat itself!

Acknowledgement

I would like to acknowledge the support of both Neil and Gavin, who in different ways, both assisted me through some particularly difficult times, and without such considered help this book would not have been written.

In the future, when my next book is published, I truly hope that I may be able to acknowledge the support of my family, which to date, sadly, have been absent without leave.

However, one always lives in hope!

About the Author

John Rees has practiced as a chiropractor for over 20 years, having retrained from his initial career as an architect.

In both his careers, he has been an observer of people, and this book provides a very clear insight into his perception of how people with different intentions interact when placed in a common environment.

Chapter 1 – The Telephone Call

The telephone rang at midday at Silkmoor Chiropractic Clinic on a bright warm Summers day. Dr. David Roseman, the resident chiropractor, answered the call. David was not only the resident chiropractor at Silkmoor Chiropractic Clinic, but also the practice manager, the company secretary, the telephonist, and the general dog's body.

David was a 52-year-old divorcee who had owned a chiropractic clinic in Silkmoor for fifteen years, which, at one time, employed seven members of staff and clinicians. Now, following his divorce some three years earlier, he worked as a sole practitioner and sole staff member of Silkmoor Chiropractic Clinic.

Twelve years earlier, David had arrived in Silkmoor with his wife, Susan, and their five-week-old daughter Eleanor. Susan, like David, was a chiropractor and, in fact, the more senior practitioner of the two. They had both moved up from London, to start a practice in the north so that they could be closer to Susan's parents, who stated that they would kindly help with childcare, whilst David and Susan were looking to build their new chiropractic practice.

They had met at chiropractic college in Bournemouth soon after Susan had graduated and on David's first day as a student at the college.

Despite being an architect, and already holding a degree, and thus already proving his academic ability to attain the necessary similar level of academic resource required to successfully attain a chiropractic qualification, David had been informed that it was a requirement to do a two-week "Bridging Course" before being eligible to start the first year of the chiropractic course. This course took place in the two weeks immediately prior to the commencement of the new academic college year.

Hence, on the day that David and Susan met, the college was ostensibly closed, accepting the three students on the Bridging Course, and those graduates and undergraduates working in the college patient clinic throughout their final year in the academic Summer recess.

Susan, who was a slim, attractive blonde-haired woman in her late 20s, was the girlfriend of the tutor in charge of the Bridging Course.

"Silkmoor Chiropractic Clinic, good afternoon," said David, in his dulcet-toned voice, which many had suggested he should use to good effect, doing voice-over work and presenting a radio programme. (He had always wondered whether this actually meant that he had a great voice to listen to, or whether they were saying that he definitely did not have the face for television!)

The lady's voice, on the other end of the phone, was difficult to hear as she was clearly speaking on a hands-free phone whilst driving with her driver's side window down.

"Hello, yes, I wonder if you can help me. I am looking to make an appointment with a chiropractor, to see if someone can sort out my neck pain".

"Certainly. When would you be looking to make an appointment?" replied David.

"Do you have any appointments this afternoon, by any chance?" replied the lady, who clearly appeared to be in need of attention sooner rather than later.

"Yes, I could see you this afternoon. What time would suit you?"

"Well, I'm on my way back from Manchester, and at the moment, I am just coming off the M60 onto the M62. So it will take me an hour from now."

"What time is it now," said David looking at the clock on the computer.

"It's just after 12.00", replied the lady.

"Okay, well, I could see you at 2.00 p.m. if that would suit you?"

"Yes, that would be perfect," the woman replied.

"Good. Can I take your name and contact number, please?"

"It's Jennifer Dolton, and my contact number is 07719241501".

"Perfect, thank you. Do you know where we are?"

The conversation continued whilst David described how to get to the clinic and outlined the duration of the initial consultation, including treatment and the fees.

Silkmoor Chiropractic Clinic had, for the last 8 years, resided in a large Victorian property, a couple of minutes walk from the railway station, and five minutes from the town centre. David and Susan had purchased the property to expand their growing business.

When they first arrived in Silkmoor, David and Susan had set up their clinic on the side of a relatively new medical centre. Being new to the area and not knowing anyone, the sitting, juxtaposed to the town's two GP practices, was perfect. Patients visiting the two large practices within the main body of the building had to walk passed the entrance to the clinic from the car park.

Although, due to the ignorance and general disinterest of the 12 GPs in the adjacent practices, in regards to what chiropractic was, no patients were referred to the clinic by the GPs. But because patients to the Medical Centre perceived that as Silkmoor Chiropractic Clinic was located in the same building as the GP's, there must have been an association; together with the quizzical nature of the passers-by, the practice built rapidly.

It was not until David and Susan had been commissioned by the NHS, that the GPs next door became prepared to condone chiropractic clinics. This is despite the fact that the second most common complaint presented to a GP was a musculoskeletal one. A part of medicine that, in their five years as undergraduate medical students, spent less than 5 weeks studying. Whereas their fellow chiropractic students studied for 5 years on musculoskeletal medicine alone.

Sadly, David and Susan had divorced some five years earlier. The divorce had been of Susan's making, although she never openly and conclusively informed David of her reasons for wanting the divorce. Susan had chosen to remain in the clinic that they had both set up for a period of four years after the divorce, which caused David a fair degree of emotional concern.

This was a woman who had stated when telling David that she wanted a divorce, that she had taken four years before announcing her desire to divorce David to get her head around her emotions and to detach herself from her commitments and feelings towards him, to be able to come to such a decision. But had then, despite the timeframe it had taken her, presumed that David would accept and adopt her wishes, without discussion or any consideration of reconciliation, with immediate effect, and also assumed that it would be totally acceptable to remain working in the clinic, almost as if nothing material had occurred between them, without any consideration for the emotional turmoil that might create for David, by being in close proximity to her in a small clinic.

Divorce comes in so many different forms and is so unique to the particular couple involved, that it is impossible to categorise divorce in a generic way psychologically. The variety within the personalities of the participants within a marriage and the circumstances, and consequences that arise within the relationship, generate such a myriad of emotions that a meaningful appraisal, beyond each specific divorce, is somewhat arbitrary.

That said, the emotion that David experienced on the morning of May 18th, 2002, when he was stood at the head of the aisle, and turned to greet his prospective wife, was not the emotion that he believed would illustrate that the decision he had made to ask Susan to marry him, was one that, had it been the correct choice, he would have been feeling, at that time.

His emotion was somewhat unique in that he clearly knew where he was and what was happening, but he could not believe that it was him that was standing there, taking these vows with this individual. He felt that he was in a surreal play, where the lead actor had called in sick on the morning of the film shoot and that, as the understudy, he had been required to step into the lead role. At some point during the ceremony, David was expecting and also hoping to hear the voice of the director called, "Cut, that's a wrap. We can go with that. Well done, David, great effort, and many thanks for stepping in at the last moment. We will need you for all the rest of the wedding breakfast scenes today for continuity if that is okay with you?"

Regrettably, after that unnerving experience on his wedding day, David felt that his marriage to Susan was fated not to be the most fulfilling, or emotionally satisfying, or rewarding that was meant to be the case. However, being a man of honour, who believed that if one has taken certain oaths in front of friends and family and contractually agreed to act in a manner towards someone else, then one was duty bound to uphold that contract for as long as was necessary.

Certainly, when a matter of weeks later, Susan informed David that they were expecting their first child, David's sense of duty to uphold his contractual side of the marriage agreement became entrenched.

Eleanor was born exactly nine months to the day after the wedding, causing David and Susan to smile readily when they calculated how productive their wedding night had been.

David readily recalls Eleanor's first moments. Once the umbilical cord was cut, David was handed Eleanor, who, quite naturally, had cried and balled her eyes out from the time that she had been delivered. However, at the moment that she was put into David's arms, still crying incessantly, with her eyes tightly shut, she fleetingly opened her eyes, looked deeply and meaningfully into David's eyes, and then, almost in a gesture of contentment, realising that she was safe and secure in her father's arms, closed her eyes as rapidly as she had opened them, stopped crying instantly, and immediately fell fast asleep in his arms.

Daniel arrived two and a half years later, a matter of days after David, Susan, and Eleanor had moved to a prestigious, large four-bedroomed family home on the favoured north side of the river in Silkmoor.

David and Susan had been able to purchase the house, consequent to two pieces of good fortune. The first being the ability, at the time, for professionals to self-certify their income and thus facilitate a mortgage that, in harsher financial climates, was not available. The second was the fact that David had been left an unmortgaged property in his mother's will that he was able to sell, which allowed him to put a large deposit down on the house that they had found and imagined to be perfect for raising the family in and to accommodate grandchildren, very satisfactorily for years thereafter.

Susan was a very capable chiropractor and a very charming, sensitive, and witty individual. However, due to a very unfortunate experience in her late teenage years that resulted in her having severe psychological issues in regards to her own self-worth and self-confidence as a woman, particularly in regards to relationships with men, she never managed to become the fulfilment of femininity and womanhood that she physically and intellectually, most definitely had the capacity to do. Her lack of femininity, which any psychologist worth his salt would appraise as being suppressed by her early life experience, was never given the opportunity to emerge and thus to allow Susan to fulfil her eminent potential. This diminution in her personality and character had a material effect on the level and depth of relationship that she could achieve with any man, including her husband, David.

Sadly, due to the experiences that David was exposed to in his childhood, he too lacked self-worth and self-esteem, which any casual observer would not perceive to be understandable due to his erudite, intellectual, socially engaging, and outgoing manner.

David was an only child who was brought up in a family where his parents regularly fought both physically and verbally. Many a time, early in his childhood, he would be woken in the depth of the night by the sound of his mother cursing and swearing at his father whilst in the process of kicking him out of bed.

His mother's outbursts usually followed a casual interaction she had had with someone who she had met in the local community that day. Due to the nature of his father's business, running a successful building firm, his role in a local male voice choir, which had toured the rural locality for over 30 years, and had recently celebrated its 3,000th performance, as well as him being chairman of the local football league, for the last 30 years, Jack Roseman was extremely well known in the surrounding community. Thus, it was not difficult to come across someone who knew him and who would happily engage in conversation about him, or had heard about events that he had been involved in, or associated with. Most, if not all, the stories and comments recounted to Rena Roseman about her husband would have been in complementary and flattering tones.

However, Rena Roseman was a woman who had always wished to have made a name for herself on the stage, but despite being a very accomplished pianist, she never achieved her desired aims, and thus would often inject drama and excess pathos into the most menial of events or situations, in an attempt to presume, that her life had much more gravitas, and importance, than the day to day events that she was subject to, actually facilitated.

The result was that Rena would happily misconstrue, re-invent or drastically accentuate a very benign story that she had been told that involved her husband, such as to regularly conclude that he was having extramarital affairs, with nearly half the female community within a twenty-mile radius of his home.

This facilitated Rena to become incensed by her husband's perceived adultery, such as to throw violent tantrums in his direction, at will.

It was commonplace, when David was between the ages of five to ten, for the Rosemans to go out for a drive on a Saturday or Sunday, often to a local place of interest. Regrettably, but invariably, within a very few miles of leaving home, Rena would have subjected her husband to a diatribe of vitriolic accusations, based on an apparent conversation she had had a few days before with someone she had met in a local town or village.

As Jack was effectively captive in his own car, Rena was able to continue the diatribe for as long as she wished. Jack's standard response was to keep silent, not show any emotion, and keep driving to their intended destination. As it was Rena's sole intent to raise a reaction from Jack to her accusations, the fact that he persistently remained silent, did not dissipate the situation at all, far from it. It only antagonised, aggravated, and angered Rena even more, such that she was caused to change her tactics to get the necessary reaction.

The one recourse that David's mother regularly used to attempt to ensure that a response was forthcoming from her husband, was to state that she wanted him to stop the car, such that she could get out. Of course, Jack ignored Rena's indignant requests, such as to escalate the interaction to a level where Rena would state that if he did not stop the car, she would just get out as it was moving. Being a rational and practical man, Jack realised the stupidity of such a proposal and continued driving. Feeling once again undermined by her husband's continued failure to be provoked into a reaction, or response, Rena would then open the passenger door of the car whilst moving at speeds of 50-60mph., pretending to make movements to leave the car, in a vane attempt to cause her husband into a response.

The only response forthcoming was from an ever more petrified child, who like his father, was captive to this enactment, sat in the back of the car. Quite naturally, at the age of 5-10 years old, David had no comprehension that his mother was bluffing. At such an age, a child is only capable of believing that what is being said by his mother is a statement of truth. Consequently, all he could envisage was his mother choosing to throw herself from a moving car and the imminent death that would befall her.

Naturally, therefore, David became intensely anxious, perplexed, and emotionally concerned at the proposed actions of his mother, resulting in him pleading with her through his tears, not to jump. Eventually, Rena rescinded her intended actions, in order to placate her child, and somehow the whole antagonistic event dissipated, allowing Jack to continue to drive to the intended destination and the family to experience their day as originally planned.

One thing that did interest David when he occasioned himself to assess his mother's "attempts" to jump from the car, was that they only ever happened on the outward journey and always within 10 miles of home. Consequently, David felt much more relaxed on the journey home from a day out with his parents.

These numerous and particularly horrible, negative emotional experiences throughout his childhood had not set David up to be a confident, self-assured individual, far from it. They caused him to believe that much, if not all, of the grief between his parents, must be something to do with him and perhaps even his fault. The result was that he was always his own worst enemy growing up, and he believed that he was never able to do the right thing and, more importantly, did not deserve to have anything relationship-wise that was stable, comforting, loving, reassuring, or fulfilling.

This belief in his lack of self-worth lay deep within David's psychology and perpetuated into his marriage, such that he found himself wanting to act in such a manner as to destroy the love and goodwill within it, projected by Susan, and hence, once it failed, to comfort himself in a slightly masochistic manner, thus proving to himself that he was not worthy of something caring and loving and meaningful.

Regrettably, once the marriage did unsurprisingly fail, he found himself being immensely resentful and remorseful of his negative contribution towards the psychology of the marriage, and its clear demise, such that he suffered a severe and lengthy period of depression that, on more than one occasion, took him to the brink of considering suicide.

It was due to his long history of psychological trauma as a child and the resultant negative emotions that he, therefore, portrayed upon himself, and the failure in all of his previous relationships, that caused him to become unduly needy and flattered by the attention of an attractive woman, who may be kind enough to give him some attention.

Just before 2.00 pm., the clinic entrance door opened, and a very elegant, demure, red-headed woman, stylishly dressed, breezed into the Reception. Her beauty was clear for all to see, and from the way that Jenny Dolton carried herself, any observer could tell that she knew that she was attractive.

She was dressed in a tancoloured dress, that fell to just above the knee. The neck was V lined, and the top button of the dress was open such as to expose a hint of cleavage. Her heels clicked as they walked across the oak-lined floor of Reception towards the desk.

David greeted her with a clipboard that held the two forms that needed to be filled out by any new patient to the clinic.

As he shook Jenny's hand, the smell of her perfume, which she had clearly just reapplied before leaving her car, filled the air.

"Hello, you must be Jenny", David smiled, as he handed over the clipboard. "Nice to meet you."

David motioned Jenny to a seat in the waiting area, and once she had sat down, started to explain what was required to fill out the forms. Despite the fact that David was drawing her attention to specific elements of the form, he noticed, in his peripheral vision, that she seemed more intent on looking him up and down, instead of focusing on the detail of the forms.

Once the explanation regarding the forms was completed, David returned to the reception desk to allow time for Jenny Dolton to fill in and sign the forms.

"Right, I think I've filled in all I can. It's difficult to remember all the accidents and operations one has had throughout one's life," Jenny said, somewhat coyly, at the same time flicking one side of her shoulder-length hair behind her shoulder and smiling sweetly.

Whether in a social or a professional situation, David did what every man has been conditioned to do when meeting an attractive woman. Whilst engaging in conversation, he had glanced down to ascertain whether there was a ring of any description on Jenny's third finger. When a man espies a wedding or engagement ring, the woman's status is obvious.

David had always been curious about the particular situation where, particularly, women in their mid-twenties to mid-forties wore a less distinguishable ring on that finger. Did it mean that they wished to give men the impression that they were unavailable when they were actually single, or were they attached, but the nature of the relationship was somewhat less traditional than was generally perceived?

The involuntary glance had caused David to notice that his new patient was engaged, and the size of the diamond on the ring could not go unnoticed.

"Please follow me". David ushered Jenny into his treatment room, which was a very well-proportioned south-facing room with a large bay window. Being an old Victorian house, the ceiling was high, and a very detailed ceiling cornice ornated the junction with the wall.

Beyond the obvious feature of the bay window, the centrepiece was the royal blue leather-covered treatment table. Chiropractors use a motorized table that has a number of different moving parts, to assist in undertaking various treatments. This is one of the main differences between a chiropractor and an osteopath, who is also a musculoskeletal therapist. Osteopaths, for some reason, use a flat plinth with a cut out at one end for the patient to attempt to comfortably house their nose.

The other main element within the treatment room was the ash-veneered consultation desk.

When he had originally designed and built the first clinic, David used his skills as an architect to design the consultation desks. Both Susan and David had wished to ensure that they engaged with their patients immediately during the first part of the consultation, the history taking.

To this end, one of the short sides of the table had been designed with a scallop taken out. The patient would sit here, with a sense of warmth, as the curve of the table received them. On one of the long sides of the desk, a shallower, longer scallop had been designed. This would allow the clinician to be partially turned towards the patient whilst asking questions and taking notes. An illustration of the attention to detail of David's design work; the two consultation desks were mirror images of each other due to Susan being right-handed and David left.

The first question David always asked his new patient was whether this was the first time the patient had been to a chiropractor. The second:-

"Where did you hear about us?'

"When I was on my drive back from Manchester, I rang Directory Enquiries and asked for a number of any chiropractors in the Silkmoor area, and they suggested your practice. I asked them to put me through, and then we spoke."

"So, what is the nature of your problem," David asked.

"For the last three weeks, I have had severe neck pain, and it seems to be getting worse. I left it for a while, as I thought it would just go away as soon as it arrived. But I am going on holiday in three weeks, and I don't want to be in this pain while I am on holiday."

"Oh, where are you going on holiday?" David asked.

"Portugal," responded Jenny.

"Nice. How long for?".

"Two weeks", replied Jenny.

For the next 15 minutes, David asked questions, specifically about a history of a patient presenting with acute neck pain. For reference, most patients believe that, in a medical situation, acute means severe pain and that chronic means a lesser low grade of pain. In the medical world, acute and chronic refer to the time period that the patient has had the condition, not its severity. Although there is some flexibility as to the exact definition of the time periods between medical professions, it is generally recognized that "acute" means less than six weeks, and "chronic" means any period longer than six weeks.

"Okay, we have completed the specific questions relating to your neck, but as you have come here straight off the street, I have to go through a series of screening questions to ensure that you have come to the right place."

"Ok".

(Chiropractors are what is known as Primary Healthcare Practitioners. In other words, the same as a GP, in that any patient can book directly with a chiropractic clinic, attend, and be seen by a chiropractor, without the need for a GP, or any other medical practitioner, to screen the patient before the consultation.

Consequently, a chiropractor has to have the same level of general diagnostic skill as a GP).

"Thank you for that. The next stage is the examination. Now on this first visit, we need to screen you overall musculoskeletally because, although your pain is in your neck, upper back, and right shoulder, the actual causation may not be in the region where the pain is felt. Therefore, I am going to pop out of the room and, in the meantime, ask you to undress, down to your underwear, keeping your underwear on, of course, and put on this gown. The Velcro goes at the back. When you are ready and dressed in the gown, open the door, and I will come in and examine you."

"Okay, thank you. Is this the only colour you have?" Jenny asked with a cheeky smile.

David smiled back and, without saying anything, left the room. After a couple of minutes, Jenny opened the door, and as he came back in, David asked the new patient to stand to the side of the treatment couch, facing the window. David stood behind her and informed her that he was going to open the back of her gown and observe her from head to toe.

The examination lasted approximately 15 minutes, the result being that David had diagnosed that there were no neurological issues. Her neck pain did not relate to any irritation of a nerve root coming out from between the vertebrae in the neck. The symptoms, including those in the shoulder, are related to "Upper Crossed Syndrome." This is a condition well known to chiropractors, and is very common in young executives, who work long hours, drive not inconsiderable distances during their working week, and are stressed by the demands of their job.

The symptoms are predominantly caused by "anterior head carriage", where the head is held forward, due to working on a computer, or a laptop. This results in the shoulders moving forward with the head, leading to shortness and tightness of the pectoral muscles. The muscles that hold the shoulder blades back to the spine, the rhomboids, will therefore be strained, causing a reduction in movement of the upper thoracic spine. Anterior Head Carriage also stresses the extensor muscles of the neck, and therefore, in time, they tighten, reducing the movement of the joints of the neck. The lack of movement in the neck, therefore, refers pain in the muscular areas that are also served by the nerves that innervate the neck muscles. This will mean shoulder and upper arm pain is also possible.

"Due to the severity of the condition, I would imagine that we would need to see you a couple of times a week for the next three to four weeks. At which time I would hope you to be between 60-80% better".

"Oh, I was hoping it would feel better before I go on my holiday in three weeks," Jenny said hopefully and with an element of concern in her voice.

"Well, I am not saying that it won't, but I cannot guarantee that it will be exactly where you wish it to be by the time you go on holiday. But I will do all I can to improve it as much as possible, David explained. "Okay, if you can lie on your front and put your head down there, and put your forearms on those pads beside the headpiece, then I can start the treatment," David requested whilst illustrating the areas of the bench that he wished his patient to lie on.

Working as a chiropractor, the clinician is always in a potentially precarious position. They are working one to one with a patient, and the nature of the work is such that they undertake it, such that they need to work within the personal private zone of patients, which is generally only reserved for family and close intimate friends.

To dissipate any possibility of the perception of social discomfort, David always engages his patients in conversation. Not only attempting to personalize the treatment, by finding out more about the patient, but to ensure that they might be somewhat distracted from the pain that can occur during treatment, by focusing on other matters.

"So, where do you work as an Occupational Therapist?" David asked.

"Well, at the moment, I am just working part-time, as I have a couple of private clients in Manchester, where I was today, who I visit on a weekly basis. I used to work for the local authority in Lancashire, but I am starting a new job at the Leeds General Infirmary after my holiday".

"Are those your children on the wall?" she asked.

"Yes," replied David.

"How old are they?"

"Eleanor is 13, and Daniel is 11".

"They're lovely names. Are you married?" Jenny continued.

In his 15 years in practice, David had never been asked by any patient what his marital status was. Clearly, when Susan worked at the clinic, everyone knew that it was a husband and wife practice, and perhaps there was no need to ask such a question. But Susan had left and set up her own clinic in another part of the town three years earlier, and none of the new patients since, male or female, had ventured such a forward question.

"No, I'm divorced", David replied.

David completed the soft tissue work and adjusted the thoracic spine.

"Can you lie on your back now, please?"

Jenny turned over and lay with her head on the headpiece. David took her neck in his hands and gently massaged the muscles of the back of the neck. Following a couple of simple stretches, he informed her that that was all that he wished to do for the first treatment.

David directed Jenny to get dressed and, when she was ready, to come to the Reception, so that she could make another appointment.

In a few minutes, Jenny arrived at the Reception, paid for the initial consultation, and booked follow-up appointments for Monday and Thursday of the next week.

Chapter 2 – The Interest

Before moving to Silkmoor, David and Susan had worked for a chiropractic practice in South London. Susan worked in the Orshington clinic and David in the Beckford. But shortly after they had started in their respective clinics, they realized that the owners of the clinic did not share the same philosophy as them, and it would probably not be long-term employment.

Whilst considering where in the country they would like to set up a clinic, David had decided to work as a locum, so he could become more knowledgeable as to the manner by which various clinics were run.

The move to West Yorkshire from South London had been a strange occurrence. Being listed on the national register for chiropractic locums, David had been contacted by a GP who worked in Pudlingley, West Yorkshire. In addition to his medical practice, he owned an alternative therapy clinic also in Pudlingley.

In July 2002, the phone rang in the penthouse apartment that David and Susan were renting in Bromley.

"Hello, good afternoon. How can I help?" said David.

"Is that Dr Roseman?" asked a well-spoken male voice with a mild hint of a Yorkshire accent.

"Yes, it is. Who is this, please, and how can I help," David replied.

"My name is Philip Pargetter, Dr. Philip Pargetter, and I have got your name from the national chiropractic locum list. I was wondering if you would like to come and work in our Pudlingley Clinic for a few weeks?"

"That's very kind of you, and thank you for making contact Philip, but my wife is 3 months pregnant, and I don't feel that it would be appropriate to move to the Leeds area, to work during the week whilst the pregnancy is ongoing. But thank you for contacting me, and I am sorry that I cannot be of help. I wish you well in your search to find someone appropriate. Goodbye".

A couple of weeks later, David received another telephone call from Dr Pargetter, asking whether he had had a change of mind. David was somewhat bemused to have received a second call, particularly from a GP, and also so soon after the earlier one. The reason for not wanting to take up the position had been due to Susan's pregnancy. She was still pregnant, and he presumed that a GP would be aware that the natural gestation of pregnancy was nine months, and the fact that when Pargetter had rung two weeks earlier, he had been informed that Susan was in the early part of the pregnancy, he would have been able to surmise that the situation had not changed, beyond Susan now being a few weeks further on in her pregnancy. Not wanting to be disrespectful, David thanked Pargetter for his continued interest but clearly stated that his opinion, in regards to the job, had not altered and would not do so for the foreseeable future.

Despite this conversation, less than two weeks later, David received another call, this time from a lady who said that she was Philip Pargetter's mother and wanted to invite David to be the locum at the practice in Pudlingley. Even though the fact that nothing had changed with Susan's pregnancy, the persistence from the Pargetter practice sparked an interest in David that caused him to agree to come up to assess the suitability of working in West Yorkshire, whilst Susan was still pregnant.

David spent two weeks working in Pudlingley whilst staying with his in-laws in Manchester. On one very warm summer's afternoon, when the clinic was not busy, he chose to meander his way back to Manchester, going via places that he had heard of when he was down south. He drove towards Ossingley, which he knew about from the fact that, for many years, they had had a strong rugby team. On arrival in the town, he was surprised at how small it was, considering the level at which Ossingley played. From Ossingley, he drove a few miles down the road to Silkmoor, and followed his nose around some very affluent streets lined with very prestigious properties.

Silkmoor is in part built on the side of a hill, and in moving up the hill, David arrived at a point overlooking the town, with the Bull and Baby rocks on his right, whilst peering down on a small, but picturesque nine-hole golf course. At this point, he pulled into the side of the road, and as he surveyed the landscape of the town below, with the imposing backdrop of the large limestone rocks behind, he gave Susan a call on his mobile.

"Hi darling, how are you? How are you feeling?" David asked.

"I'm fine, just relaxing. I've had a busy day in clinic and am constantly salivating still". Susan suffered throughout her pregnancy with a rare condition that caused her to salivate constantly. It was so frequent that she even had to secrete a spittoon out of sight of her patients so that, part way through the treatment, she could surreptitiously spit into a bag without the patients being aware.

"I think I've found where we need to be. I'm standing by the side of the road overlooking Silkmoor with the Bull and Baby at my back

and a lovely-looking golf course on the side of the hill in front of me."
It's got a gorgeous feel to it, and I don't think it has a chiropractic
clinic in it".

"Oh, Silkmoor is lovely," responded Susan. "We used to come to
visit with friends when I lived up in Manchester."

A month later, during a weekend when David and Susan were
visiting her parents in Manchester, they decided to go over to
Silkmoor to see if there was anywhere to set up a clinic.

Their first port of call was a well-known West Yorkshire estate
agent called Downton, Son, and Hamley, situated in a very prominent
location at the junction of the two main shopping streets in the town.

On entering the agency, they approached a lady sitting behind a
large oak desk.

"Excuse me. We are looking to find premises, perhaps at this
stage, just a managed room, where we might be able to set up a clinic."

"Oh, I am terribly sorry. This is the residential lettings section,"
said a very well-presented lady with beautifully coiffured hair. At
this point, a man walked behind where the couple were sitting.

"Excuse me, Martin, this lady and gentleman are looking to rent
some small commercial premises in Silkmoor."

Martin was a suited man in his early fifties, who typified the
appearance of a country estate agent. "Well, it depends on how big a
premises you are looking for. There is that unit beside the medical
centre in Sprigget Lane"

"Beside a medical centre, that sounds perfect. May we have a look" asked David, getting a feeling of excitement about premises directly juxtaposed to a medical centre.

Five minutes later, they were introduced to a bare, open space of 1000 square feet on the ground floor of a building, the remainder of which was split between two medical practices. The position of the property entrance meant that patients visiting the medical centre would have to walk past the entrance to get to the medical centre. Both Susan and David looked longingly at each other as they could see the immense potential of positioning a new, unknown medical business in such a prominent location.

The door to the clinic opened two minutes before Jennifer Dolton was due for her second appointment.

Since the divorce, David had got rid of the other clinicians at the clinic and converted the upper two floors from treatment rooms into a self-contained flat. Due to the financial limitations that a divorce places upon one, the décor of the rooms in the flat still very much reflected the feel of treatment rooms. However, the opportunity of moving back into his own property from rented, which he had been occupying for the last two years, far outweighed the desire to redecorate.

During her first appointment Jennifer Dolton had stated that due to her moving jobs from a hospital in Lancashire to one in Leeds, she had time on her hands. One of the topics of conversation during the last treatment was cycling. David had said that he had done a lot of cycling in the past and that it was a great location to cycle, with the Dales being within spitting distance of Silkmoor.

Jenny had said that she would like to get into cycling but was unfit and, therefore, would wish to start on the flat, which was not easy in this area. David had suggested cycling along the towpath in Saltsley, which was no more than 15 minutes drive from where Jenny lived. Whilst she was paying for her initial consultation, Jenny had said that she would go for a cycle ride directly after her next appointment.

With that in mind, David was somewhat surprised at the manner by which Jenny was attired, as she entered the waiting room from the entrance lobby of the clinic, on arrival for her second appointment.

Being the only person at the clinic currently; between patients, David would sit at the computer located behind the reception desk at the end of a long thin waiting room. When he heard the entrance door open, he would get up from reception, walk towards the entrance, and generally greet the forthcoming patient halfway down the waiting area. He would direct the patient with a motion of his hand to turn around and walk towards the treatment room, on the other side of the entrance lobby.

However, on this occasion, on hearing the door open, David, as normal, walked from behind the reception desk to greet Jenny in the waiting room. When she appeared in the waiting room, Jenny was dressed in a low-cut flame red summer dress that fell mid-thigh. She was well made up and wore lipstick to match the colour of her dress. Not the sight that one might expect to greet with a prospective cycle ride to follow. On entering the waiting room, Jenny walked purposefully up to David, turned one hundred and eighty degrees, and placed her right hand around David's waist.

In 13 years of being a chiropractor, a patient had never greeted David in such a fashion. A handshake was generally the most usual. Perhaps a mild peck on the cheek from a longstanding patient who he had not seen for a while. But an arm around the waist was a first.

In the politest fashion possible, David ignored the contact and directed Jenny into the treatment room. As on every other occasion where a female patient needed to be gowned, David handed the gown to the patient, directed them to undress to an appropriate amount, depending on the treatment forthcoming, and reminded them to open the door to let him back in once they were dressed accordingly.

David would then wait outside as he duly did on this occasion until Jenny opened the door and gowned as directed.

"So how has it been since the initial treatment, Jenny" David asked, as he politely directed her to lie on her front, on the bench he had lowered to best help her to get on it.

"I don't have the headaches as severely as when I first came, and the movement seems a little better," Jenny replied as she went to lie on the bench.

"Is it waking you at night?" David quizzed.

"No, but I feel it more in the evenings when I am watching television," informed Jenny with a smile.

"Often, the pain can appear worse in the evenings. This is due to the fact that during the day, the mind is focused on all the day-to-day things that concerns one, such that the signal from the areas of pain does not manage to get through if you like. However, when you are relaxing in the evening, with nothing on your mind, there is more capacity for the brain to receive the signals that the damaged tissue has been sending during the whole of the day. Hence it appears to be worse at night." David explained.

"That's interesting". Jenny responded.

During the treatment, the conversation covered a number of topics, including the length of time that David had lived in Silkmoor. Jenny also asked some personal questions in relation to David's divorce and ex-wife. Due to the professional relationship, David found himself having to be sensitive to his response to a woman asking very detailed questions of ostensibly a stranger.

Having been confused by the attire that Jenny arrived in, considering the understanding of her going for a cycle ride directly afterwards, David asked if his patient had had a busy morning.

"Oh no, I've come straight from home," she said.

"So, are you not going for a cycle later? It's a lovely day out there and seems perfect for a cycle". Asked David quizzically.

"Oh no, I am going directly after here," Jenny affirmed.

Since his divorce, David had suffered severely from depression and had had regular suicidal thoughts. He had lost the skill to assess whether a woman had an interest in him. If asked, he would suggest that, due to being an only child, and being sent to a single-sex boarding school, he had never assimilated the subtle signs that a woman emits, whatever their feelings.

However, David felt himself questioning why a woman who had not been at work prior to the appointment and who was going for a cycle ride directly after the appointment would turn up dressed to the nines, wearing quite striking make-up, unless she was looking to make an impression. Due to his recent state of mind and lack of self-esteem, he comforted himself that Jenny was a woman, like many northern women, who would never leave a trip to the bathroom without reapplying lipstick.

Jenny paid, made another appointment, and left with a look and a warm smile over her shoulder.

Three days later, just prior to her appointment, Jenny walked into the waiting area, again dressed in a fashion inconsistent with a woman not working and who was just about to receive treatment. However, David thought nothing of it, but despite being in professional mode, could not but feel a sense of pleasantness that Jenny looked as she did.

On the second appointment, Jenny walked purposefully into the waiting room. This time, however, she was able to surprise David in a different manner. Not the arm around the waist this time, but the presentation of a silver foil-covered baking dish.

"I thought you might like this. I know that you live by yourself, and I was making a pasta bake last night and thought I would just make a little more for you," she said with a broad warm smile on her face."

"Oh, right, thank you," stuttered David, not able to disguise his shock at such a presentation, as well as he felt, as the professional in the room, he should have done.

"Right, right, right, uh, thank you - okay," he said in a slightly spluttering fashion. "Shall we go through"?

A similar routine unfolded as in the previous two sessions.

"So you said that you were going on holiday to Portugal in a few weeks' time. Where are you going exactly?"

"Well, we are going to a wonderful location to get married," Jenny replied.

"Oh ok, I had noticed the engagement ring. So, is everything organized? It must be difficult to co-ordinate everything, and be assured that it is as you would wish from so far afield, isn't it?" said David.

"We have employed a wedding planner, and he seems to know what he is doing," Jenny stated nonchalantly.

"So that all sounds particularly exciting!" David said warmly.

Unexpectedly Jenny's response was not instant, and when it came, it was not exactly overly effusive. "Yes, I suppose," she responded with an air of mild dismissiveness.

At the time of commencing this line of conversation, David had presumed that it would affect a very positive resource for continual discussion. Talking about the dress; her fiancé; the location; how they had met; their future plans, and all the things associated with the excitement of starting a new life. Jenny had been married before and had two mature children, both girls in their early twenties. However, the nature of her response floored David's desire to continue this direction of the conversation.

The consultation finished with the usual agreement to a follow-up appointment.

Being a Wednesday in the Summer meant that David played cricket in the evening for a team known as the Overoptomists. The name gives a good indication of the principles behind those who were members. The team had been set up by a group of Dads whose children had gone to the same NSPCC association. As is common, the mothers of the children had a clear maternal affiliation and therefore bonded easily and quite readily. The men, on the other hand, having bumped into each other whilst occasionally picking their respective children up from school, had decided to do certain sporting activities together so as to generate a similar bond, as experienced by their respective wives. In the early years, they had played rugby, cycled every Tuesday night into the Dales, and started a cricket team. With the passing of time, and increased wisdom, they had knocked rugby on the head, but cycling and cricket had persisted.

David had been invited to join the cricket team some six years previously, by a local doctor and had been credited with one of the most memorable finishes to an Overoptomists' match in their history. With 3 balls remaining, David came into bat, the team requiring eight to win. The opposition was made up of the congregation of one of the local churches, St. Maudelin's, led by their enigmatic vicar Father Michael. Those parishioners of St. Maudelin's, who made up their cricket team and who only also played once a year against the Overoptomists, played for the Overoptomists the rest of the season.

Prior to being called to the cloth, Father Michael, the vicar at St. Maudelin's, who was a keen off-spin bowler, had been a bookies clerk, and consequently, there was nothing that he did not know about betting, to such an extent that he, and two of his regular choristers had been banned from all the betting shops within a 10-mile radius of the town, due to their persistent success at cleaning up with their numerous weekly bets.

The bowler for the final over had played professional cricket for Nottinghamshire in his day and bowled, on a length, at the top of the off stump, with the regularity of Glenn McGrath. Thus, as expected, Pendleton's first ball to David held line and length on the off stump. David half-blocked and half-punched the shot. In attempting a single, he was denied by Pendleton's bear hug, restricting David to a standstill. Thus, two balls remained, and eight were still needed. The penultimate ball, at pace but straying down the leg side; a lucky contact of the bat off his legs, and the ball raced away to the deep square leg boundary, thumping into the base of the terrace, directly in front of the pavilion; four being added to the score. One ball left, four needed. Pendleton smiled a knowing smile over his shoulder to David as he walked back to his mark. A slight amendment of the field. More time taken to add to the tension, rather than to effect any real alteration to his team in the field. With the sun setting, Pendleton commenced his run. David knew it would be pitching directly on the middle stump, and therefore he had to make contact with a straight bat. Sure enough, right on the middle stump, but slightly overpitched. David leaned forward and remembered saying to himself, *"just make contact David, just make contact"*. To the surprise of all concerned, none more than David, he had somehow hit a slightly overpitched ball off the middle of the bat, for a perfect 'on drive' that raced along the ground, to the longest boundary, on the ground, in front of the scoreboard. From certain defeat to assured victory, a county bowler muted, and the Overoptomists had one of their best finishes in a match ever.

Unfortunately, on this particular Wednesday, due to the inclement weather, the match had been cancelled at the last moment, and David found himself going for a consoling beer in a pub regularly frequented by a friend. At this time of evening, just after 6.00p.m on a Wednesday, the pub was all but empty. Having ordered and paid for his pint, David sat at a table in the middle of the pub. A few minutes later, the door to the pub opened, and who should walk in but Jenny Dolton, accompanied by a male, somewhat older than herself. David presumed that this was the fiancée. She smiled and walked past without speaking. Her companion looked like a very gruff, uncommunicative individual and stared at David as he passed.

The couple ordered a drink and sat a distance from David, at a table on the other side of the pub. However, David noticed that although the companion was sat such that he could not be seen by David, Jenny had positioned herself so that she could be seen and see David.

During the time it took David to complete his drink, he noticed that Jenny had glanced in his direction a number of times. When David was ready to leave, he felt it would be rude not to acknowledge a patient formally. He walked over to the table occupied by the couple, that was on his way out to the car park.

"Hello, this is a bit of a coincidence," David addressed Jenny.

"Yes, I suppose it is. This is Simon. Simon, this is David".

"Should I know you?" the fiancée responded in a very dismissive and arrogant tone.

David's initial response was to respond in a similarly dismissive and unfriendly manner. But he refrained, as he was in the company of a patient and chose to respect the nature of that relationship.

"No, I don't think so," replied David with a smile, but wondering at the same time how on earth Jenny had chosen to get engaged to a gruff, unpleasant character like Simon.

On leaving the pub and whilst driving home, David considered the possibility of meeting Jenny in a pub, in Silkmoor on a Wednesday evening, in a town some 6 miles from where she lived, particularly as there were three very pleasant pubs, within walking distance of their home in Burton-on-Aire. Maybe he was just being paranoid!

Chapter 3 – Crossing The Line

The day following the impromptu meeting in the pub, David noticed that Jenny was his first patient in the afternoon following lunch.

As usual, David started at 7.00 a.m. with his first appointment. From the inception of the clinic, David and Susan had decided to open from 7.00 a.m. to 7.00 p.m. This would allow them to offer appointments to patients who worked in Silkmoor, and also those who commuted to the local conurbations of Leeds and Bradford, without the need to take time off work. They believed that this would assist in ensuring patients' compliance to attend their appointments and therefore ensure that they could enable the most effective treatment regime, enabling the patients' conditions to improve more quickly.

As their eldest child, a daughter, Eleanor was only 5 weeks old when they arrived in Silkmoor, they had also chosen not to work at the weekends, as this would impinge on family time. Additionally, due to the need to see new patients, initially twice a week, to effect the best treatment outcome, they had chosen not to open on a Wednesday. Patients coming on a Monday were best seen on a Thursday, and those arriving on a Tuesday were on the Friday of the same week. Thus, patients seen on a Wednesday would ideally need to be seen on a Saturday, which would conflict with family time. It also would enable an associate chiropractor to join the clinic and have the freedom of having his or her own clinic on a Wednesday and a Saturday.

At around 11.00 a.m. David received a text from Jenny asking whether she could be seen any earlier than 2.00 pm. appointment.

Jenny had his mobile number, as David had had reason to text her in the week previously, as she had been late for an appointment.

David responded by saying that as it was the day after a Bank Holiday, he had a full patient list and that the only time that he could see her would be at lunchtime at 1.00 p.m.

The reply text said, "Oh, I don't want to take up your lunchtime, but I'd be happy to take both appointment times, my 2.00 p.m. for my treatment, but also at 1.00 to take you to lunch."

David replied. "That's very flattering, but I will just be popping out for a quick sandwich at a local café. I'll see you at 2.00!"

The remainder of the morning was uneventful, beyond being busy. The most common complaint presented to the chiropractic clinic, related to low back pain. Often, and particularly in the early days of the clinic, patients presented who had gone back and forth to the GP, always with no positive effect or direction, beyond being told to come back in a fortnight if it had not got any better.

When the last patient of the morning had paid and made another appointment, David slipped on his coat, walked through the clinic, locked the entrance door, and walked along the road towards the nearest café that was situated in an arcade near the entrance to the railway station. It was a 3-minute walk that took him up onto Platform 2 of Silkmoor station, a walk along the length of the platform, across the bottom of both platforms, and into the café. Despite making the walk at least twice a day, for over ten years, it was still a regular occurrence for an officious station attendant to ask David for his ticket. If he had the misfortune to miss time his walk along the platform, as a train was arriving, by the time he had got to the end of the platform, he had been immersed with passengers

ad had, on more than one occasion, been verbally
by an attendant, adamant that he should produce a ticket for
journey he had not taken.

The café was owned by an Italian, who had cut his teeth in a
similarly located café, juxtaposed Kings Cross station in London.
Although Silkmoor was a minute station in comparison, the principles
of serving customers catching a train were the same. Consequently,
the café was staffed with enough people to ensure that the time taken
to produce a coffee or a sandwich, or any other simple fare, was as
expeditious as possible. The coffee was well known to be the nicest
of that sold in all the coffee shops in Silkmoor, of which there was
legion. Additionally, the tables were always maintained clean and
tidy.

David arrived at the café, and as usual, it was busy; at lunchtime
with numerous customers who were retired, who may have popped to
the post office opposite and decided on a coffee and a light lunch;
cyclists who had returned from a trip to the Dales, and office workers
who wanted a change to the standard, pre-packed lunch offerings
from Tescos and Marks and Spencers.

The staff at the café were always extremely welcoming, and if one
was a local, it gave the feel of the café equivalent to the sitcom bar in
Cheers. "Evening, everyone," the refrain from Norm Peterson as he
entered the bar every evening. – "Norm!" came the immediate refrain
from all the staff and patrons in the bar.

David regularly ordered a ciabatta sandwich and fruit juice of the
choice of the staff waiting. Today, once his food arrived, he reflected
on a very positive morning. Fifteen patients, all of whom reported
feeling better after their previous treatment. He regularly considered

the good fortune of being trained in a profession that allowed him to meet a total stranger who presented as a new patient, often in considerable pain, who had, on many occasions already, visited their GP, a physiotherapist, and others who purported to be able to help; all often to no positive benefit, who, after a few treatments with him, were able to report considerable improvement.

Due to the café being busy, David sat at a table with his back to the entrance door. It was whilst he was biting into his pastrame and salad ciabatta that he heard a voice that he recognized at exactly the same time as he felt a gentle hand on his right shoulder.

"Hello, fancy seeing you here" said the soft, soothing feminine voice. Immediately without turning to look at the person, he knew who it was. He was surprised and shocked in equal measure to being pleased. The lady sat down opposite him, saying. "Do you mind if I join you?"

Feeling very much in a cleft stick, considering that within forty-five minutes, he would be welcoming this person for her next treatment, David felt compelled to welcome Jenny to join him.

"What would you like to drink?" David asked politely.

"Oh, I don't know. What do they have?" Jenny asked, whilst smiling sweetly, clearly delighted that the café that she had guessed David would be having lunch at was the first one she had chosen to check out.

"Well, you can have a multiplicity of juices, a full menu of coffees, sandwiches, and even a couple of the chef's pasta dish".

"So, have you had a busy morning David?" Jenny asked

"Yes, it's always the case after a bank holiday too".

When he had finished his lunch, David politely excused himself from the table, stating a   need to remove patient gowns from the washing machine, before his afternoon clinic.

Jenny smiled warmly as he left.

Walking across the station concourse, David realized that he had ordered some flowers for the clinic reception from a local florist. He diverted his path and went to the florist to pick up the flowers that he bought on a weekly basis.

As was often the case, he ended up being engaged in a longer-than-usual conversation with the florist, who was always very communicative. David walked back along the pavement to the clinic with the flowers. As he walked up the steps to the clinic, he saw Jenny walking in the other direction. Still needing to remove the gowns from the tumble dryer, he quickly opened the front door, went into his treatment, put the flowers on his desk, and then rushed into the basement to get the gowns. He arrived back in the entrance lobby, gowns in hand, just as Jenny opened the clinic door.

"Hi," she said.

"Hi, Jenny," David replied, "Here's a gown, if you would just like to change, and let me in once you're ready." David directed. He opened the door to allow Jenny into the treatment room. A few moments later, the door burst open, and before he could react, Jenny had all but jumped into his arms.

"Oh, thank you, are they for me? They are beautiful?" Jenny asked in a delighted voice.

Instantly David attempted to compute what to do and what to say. If he told her the truth, then perhaps she would feel extremely deflated. But if he said that they were for her, he could be in breach of his professional code of conduct. He chose a non-descript response by saying,

"Can you lie on your front please" showing her towards the bench.

As had been the case in earlier treatments, he massaged and manipulated her upper back and massaged her neck. Then asking her to turn onto her back, he would stretch and adjust her neck.

"Oh, I meant to mention this last time. I lifted something the other day and felt a twinge partway down the right side of my chest." Jenny said.

"Oh okay, where about, exactly," asked David, whilst distracting her neck. Jenny took her left hand and pointed it to a point just below her right breast. "Do you think you could look at it, please?"

"Yes, certainly. What happened exactly? Did you hear something go?" David questioned.

In order to examine the area, David needed to lift the gown from beneath the chest area. In doing so, he put folded another gown over the chest area that would allow movement of the first gown. The resultant being that the chest would remain covered at all times, and yet the skin beneath the chest could be examined and treated.

"Would you mind putting your hand here to hold this gown, please?" David directed Jenny so that her hand would be on the gown over her chest.

"Mmm, that feels tender," David stated as he examined the costochondral musculature between the 7th and 8th rib.

"Mmm, yes, very much so". Jenny responded.

"Ok, well, it appears that you have clearly sprained or strained the muscles here. I am going to use some acupuncture needles in the area if you do not mind," David suggested.

In administering the needles, David had to be cautious on two levels. First, to ensure that the angle of input of the needle did not allow the needle to sit too deep. The pleura, the lining surrounding the lungs, sits just below the ribs and must not be punctured. The second was to ensure that the right breast remained covered.

Partway through the treatment, Jenny appeared to lift her hand off the gown protecting her right breast. Consequently, the gown slipped, exposing the breast. There was a noticeable delay before Jenny retrieved the gown and re-covered the breast. During that time, her eyes engaged with David's. The expression in her eyes appeared to say, "Did you like what you saw?".

Shortly after the treatment finished, David left the room, saying he would see Jenny in the Reception.

The few minutes that passed whilst Jenny got dressed allowed David to recompose himself.

When Jenny emerged into the waiting area, she seemed quite perplexed.

"Are you okay" David questioned.

David expected Jenny's response to relate to an apology for letting the gown slip, and was therefore immensely surprised by what she said.

"I'm meant to be getting married in ten days, but since I have met you, I am not sure if I am doing the right thing," Jenny said in a concerned, considered, and mildly melancholic tone.

"Ah, ah, well, mmm, well, what can I say?" David started in a stuttering and uncertain fashion. "You've been with Simon for more than two years, haven't you?'

"Yes" Jenny responded somewhat embarrassingly.

"You have known me less than three weeks, and you are not sure if you should continue with your wedding? Personally, I am not a psychologist, but I would think that if meeting someone for such a short period of time, at your age, makes you uncertain as to whether you want to go through with your intended wedding, then that should tell you more about what might be wrong with your current relationship, rather than what you might feel about the person you have just met. You're engaged to be married. You've been together for over two years. You're a fifty-year-old woman Jenny. It's not like you're an eighteen-year-old who has come across new emotions. I'm flattered, I really am, you're a very attractive woman, and any man would be flattered, but there are a number of issues here. First, you are due to be married in less than a fortnight. So, if you would wish to change ship, you have to address that imminent elephant in the room. Secondly, I'm your chiropractor. It's a professional relationship. I cannot be your chiropractor and enter into a relationship with you. I have noticed your forwardness since you became a patient three weeks ago. Initially, I thought that you were just overtly friendly, but when I piece all the elements together with what you have just said, I realize that I should have curtailed the professional relationship a period of time ago." David paused for effect and to attempt to compute what Jenny had said and how to exit this particular situation. Clearly, on one level, due to where his head was psychologically, he wanted to explore her interest, but he was also very conscious of the boundary between a medical professional and a patient, which a clinician herself she should also have been readily aware and duly sensitive, and respectful of also.

"Now, on a personal level, I am single and getting over a very acrimonious divorce, and that has also left me vulnerable. Your attention has been somewhat cathartic for me. That is probably why I have allowed your forwardness to continue. But that has put me at risk on a professional level. So, I am afraid that I cannot see you any longer as your chiropractor." David held a kind and concerned, but stern look towards Jenny as he completed his comment.

"But I still need treatment, and I only have less than a week to get right for my wedding," Jenny responded in a hurt tone.

"Well, that is true. But I think you are conflating two different issues here. Yes, you need further treatment. But isn't it of greater concern that you are about to make what is intended to be a lifelong decision, that you seem to be very uncertain about? When will you know if you've made the right decision?" David's tone had hardened somewhat. How could anyone be trying to emotionally blackmail someone to continue treatment when they had just raised such a massive issue?

"I suppose when I walk down the aisle," Jenny said timidly.

"Jesus Christ, really! You can't be serious? So what will happen if, at the top of the aisle, you do not feel as you think you should feel? Will you ask someone to tell the organist to halt the music? Will you give your attendant your bouquet, and simply turn tail and walk back to your hotel room? Christ almighty Jenny, you're not asking everyone to turn up at Kelbrook Registery Office here. You've got friends to book flights, stay over in hotels for at least two nights in bloody Portugal, for Christ's sake."

At this point, Jenny started to cry. "Oh, what have I done? What am I going to do? What should I do? I am really all over the place with this!" The tears poured down her cheeks as, with her head bowed, she meekly looked up at David, who was now standing behind the reception desk.

"Why don't you talk to your mother about it, or to some friends, or your daughters even? They are mature women who would love to be supportive of you."

"Well, my mother and step-father hate Simon, so they would be delighted if I called it off. And my daughters," she paused, "well, I can't tell them. I'm their Mum. I need to be the strong one for them, not the other way around!" Jenny responded as she wiped tears from her eyes.

"Don't be daft. If they were teenagers or preschool children, then, of course, that would be different. But they are mature women who have had relationships go bad, who would understand your dilemma, and who would probably feel immensely privileged to be consulted on such a critical matter. For so long in a family, there has been a parent-child relationship. It has been a formative part of both parties' lives. Often when the children become adults, the family fails somewhat because neither party realizes that the roles have changed. You moved from being a supporter and supported to being mutually interested friends. You now are living life experiences similar to each other. Whereas before, your issues worked in raising a family, and theirs were school and what to do on their holidays. Now they work as do you. They have problems in relationships, as do you. So being family, you have the great opportunity to be confidantes and close friends. Why not use that gift?"

"I can't. I just can't. It would not be right," Jenny said in a defiant if unconvincing way.

"Oh, ok, so what are you going to do then?" David asked, sensing that Jenny was just looking to bumble on and not consider the massive predicament that she was moving into.

"I am sorry to be blunt, but you need to make a positive decision. At the moment, things are set up such that in less than a fortnight, you will be remarried. Everyone around you, including Simon, would have naturally presumed, as they see you walk down the aisle, having spent considerable time and effort organizing this thing, and moving job and house and location to be with this guy, that you are happy to have made the right choice, and are just taking the next step. No one, whether parent, family, or friend, is going to step in and ask a 50-year-old woman on the eve of her wedding. *"Are you sure that you're doing the right thing? Are you happy?"* No, of course not, for two reasons. First, because they naturally presume that you would not be embarking on another long-term commitment if you were not happy, as you have no reason to do so unless you are happy. Also, because, to be quite frank, Jenny, although they will be attending your wedding and looking to have a good time, in truth, they really don't care a monkeys. They, like the vast majority of people, are only interested in themselves and looking at their own navels. So, if you do not ask the questions yourself, but choose to attempt to forget these massive uncertainties, then you will only have yourself to blame and only have yourself to live with. Because, ultimately, we only ever have to live with ourselves, Jenny, don't we?" David paused to allow him to reflect on his last diatribe. Had he been too forceful? Had he been a bit too blunt? No, not really. Here, in front of him, was a woman who was due to be married in two weeks, had known him for less than three weeks, stating that she was uncertain about becoming betrothed again, due to the emotions she felt for him. No, he had not been too harsh at all.

After a lengthy silence in the conversation, that was only made the more poignant by realizing that the song being played on the radio, in the background, was a little-known hit by Elton John called "The One", which defines, quite graphically, how the woman in the song was his ultimate desire, Jenny pulled herself together.

"So, have you any recommendations for another chiropractor I could see before I go, please?" she asked furtively.

"Well, there is my ex-wife, who practices about 300 yards away. She is a very good chiropractor and is very kind, caring, and professional. Unfortunately, though, you will have to pay an initial consultation fee again as, from an insurance point of view, she has to make her own diagnosis." David said softly.

Chapter 4 - The Friendship

Jennifer Dolton had been David's last patient of the week. After she left, David closed the clinic, cashed up, locked the front door, and went upstairs to the flat where his son Daniel was playing on his X-box.

As part of the agreement, in regards to the divorce, it had been stated that the children should spend fifty percent of the time with their father. This had been agreed upon, in part to attempt to ensure that the children got as even a relationship with both parents as possible. It was very important to the children in this case, as David had been a very proactive father before the divorce. He had set the clinic up to ensure spending as much time as possible with the children, and had picked them up from school and dropped them off as many times in the week as had Susan, and thus was active in preparing their dinner and putting them to bed also.

He was also very active in engaging with them on those afternoons that he had picked them up from school, and did not come home and turn on the television and place them in front of it, and go and do his own thing.

Due to the size of the house, with four large bedrooms and a number of built-in wardrobes, it was not at all uncommon for the afternoon after school to be spent playing hide and seek, particularly in the winter months, or sledging down the field directly behind the house, after it has snowed.

One favourite game for the children was sliding down the stairs on the inflatable mattresses that David had bought for their camping trips. On one telling occasion, just after Eleanor had slid down the length of the staircase, laughing and screaming in delight, at the top of her voice; she stood up and asked, in a very mature, considered voice. "Why doesn't Mummy play with us as much as you do, Daddy?" Taken aback by the question, and not wanting to paint Susan in a bad light, he created an excuse that he hoped justified her lack of desire to play with her children. However, such a comment hit home at the time, such that he could readily recall it whilst going through the divorce and thus, consequently, ensured, as best as he could, that, at the very least, access to the children was equally apportioned. Sadly as Family Law and Divorce Law are written as to be heavily biased, not only towards the mother but, as many fathers would vouch, written against the fair-minded rights of the father, ensuring an equitable split of time spent with both parents, was not as easy to arrange and agree, as a reasonable, fair minded person should expect to be the case.

Unfortunately, but as it often happens, his ex-wife had defaulted from the agreement, and only Daniel came to stay with David, and even so, not to the level that had been agreed with the solicitors.

The fact that Daniel was in the house allowed David to deflect his attention from the interaction that had happened shortly before with Jenny Dolton.

However, over the weekend, he was able to consider the predicament in which he had found himself. He was aware that the divorce had affected him hugely psychologically. Due to his personality, he had taken the brunt of the responsibility for the failure of the marriage, which, as is the case in most divorces, is rarely down to the failure, solely of one of the parties involved. However, having built up a very successful chiropractic business, including a unique contract commissioned with the NHS, which resulted in seeing well over one hundred patients per week, buying a gorgeous family home in one of the most prestigious parts of the town, fathering two exquisite children, it came as a body blow to see ten years of immense effort, fall apart without even an explanation from his ex-wife.

Men are designed to problem solve. Not all problems thrown in front of a man are able to be solved. However, not having the opportunity to attempt to solve the problem, is as undermining for the man, as dealing with the problem itself.

Susan had given David no indication whatsoever of what was wrong with the marriage. Beyond saying that she had been unhappy for ten years, nothing was mentioned. If someone is unhappy for such a period of time, is it not incumbent on them to raise it as an issue much earlier, such that one can look to address the concerns and, if willing, attempt to rectify them? Not to do so illustrates an inherent disrespect towards the person one had taken out a solemn oath.

David knew that he would not have allowed himself to be drawn into the situation he found himself in with Jenny, if he had not been so damaged by his divorce. If she had been a single lady and if she had not been a patient, he would most probably have been very interested in her. However, he could not allow his needs as a damaged man to override his professional position. He had done the right thing and would hopefully put the interaction down to experience, and move on.

At 8.00 pm. on Sunday evening, just as he was sitting down to a roast chicken dinner with Daniel, which was a particular favourite of his son, David's phone pinged with a text message. The message was from Jenny.

"Thank you for all your thoughts and consideration. I very much respect your position and understand the stance that you have taken. However, I am still not sure what to do."

Perhaps foolishly, David chose to reply. Having discharged Jenny as a patient, he believed that he had discharged his responsibility to her as a clinician and, therefore, could offer support with a clear mind.

"I am not sure how I can help," he texted.

"Well, I haven't got anyone to talk to, and wondered if we could meet for lunch X".

David noted the 'X' at the end of the text, but chose to see it as just a friendly gesture. "Well, we could, but to what end? If you would like my advice as to what to do, then I am happy to meet and be a sounding board. But ultimately, you have to be sure in your own mind what you want to do."

"Thank you. Where would you like to meet X?" Jenny replied.

"I am free on Wednesday as it is my day off. I have to do some admin work with my secretary first thing, but we could go for lunch after."

"Okay, shall I come to the clinic then X," asked Jenny.

"Yes, if you come over at, say, 10.30-11.00, we can go from there". David proposed, with a hint of trepidation in his mind.

"Thank you, I will see you on Wednesday XX."

What did the "XX" mean? What was the text protocol? Did that mean anything more than just one "X" David cogitated?

Wednesday arrived without issue. On his days off, Wendy, who used to be a relief receptionist when the clinic had seven clinicians, often popped in to help David with keeping business accounts up to date. Wendy had been a school friend of Lucy, who had been the longstanding practice manager, and was an ideal foil to keep the reception running smoothly, on the occasions that Lucy went on holiday, or was ill.

In the short period of time that Wendy had been at the clinic, on that Wednesday, David had outlined the events of the previous three weeks.

Although Wendy was of a similar age to David, she had kindly adopted the role of elder sister since David's divorce. It was particularly obvious from her furrowed brow that Wendy had a bad feeling about this woman and this situation.

"How old is she?" Wendy asked, not hiding her dismissive disgust about the woman. "She sounds very dangerous to me. No one at that age should be acting in that way. I would be very cautious if I was you, David. She sounds like a typical bunny boiler to me."

Before David was able to respond to Wendy's statement, they both heard the door open.

Jenny walked in dressed to the nines and smiled sweetly at Wendy, who reciprocated in a way that only a woman can. Able to smile with apparent warmth, but concealing immense disregard and disgust behind the soft, sweet smile.

"Okay, Wendy, is that all alright with you then? I will be back mid-afternoon, I expect, by which time I presume you will be well gone. Are you off to Scotland this weekend?"

Wendy and her husband, Arthur, owned a small cottage beside a Loch on the western edge of Scotland. Since Arthur had started his semi-retirement, they had spent many long weekends renovating the property. Arthur had spent a lengthy career on merchant ships. In the last twenty, he had been commissioned to go and inspect ships, in all parts of the world, at the behest of various insurers.

"We haven't decided yet, as my mother is unwell, and we need to see if she needs our help," Wendy replied.

David and Jenny said their goodbyes to Wendy and walked around the front of the property, down Wilton Road, and into the courtyard behind the clinic.

"I'll drive if you would like?" David said, directing Jenny towards his Lexus.

"Oh, okay, yes, sure. But can I put my car somewhere that it is not easily seen, please? Simon is more than a little suspicious and very possessive, and I wouldn't want him to see my car parked here,". Jenny said in a very matter-of-fact manner.

A cold chill passed across David's mind. What was he getting himself into here? This guy seemed a little manic. David recalled that he thought that they were not ideally matched when he had seen them in the pub. A few days later, Tim, a friend, and David had played golf and, afterward, went up to the Bull and Baby for a bank holiday beer. Coincidentally, whilst they were sat outside, musing about how well they had both played, who should turn up for a drink, but Jenny and her fiancé? Interestingly, although she had noticed David, her fiancé had not, and so she chose not to acknowledge David. During their beer, Tim, who was sitting in view of the couple, quizzed as to what might be going on as Jenny repeatedly glanced in David's direction.

"I thought that we might go for lunch at Blunton Lodge Hotel. It's a spa hotel near Harrogate".

"Oh ok, well I only have a few hours as I have to take the dog to my Mum's, as she is looking after him whilst we are in Portugal. Is it far?"

"About 25 minutes at this time of day. It's a great place, good for a relaxing weekend break. They have invested thousands in a new spa. I understand the brief was to build the best spa in Europe. I am not sure if they have achieved it, but in this region with Leeds, Harrogate, York, and Silkmoor within a short distance, there is the right demographic to make it work."

Twenty-five minutes later, just as David had said, they were turning into the driveway towards the impressive Blunton Lodge.

Throughout his marriage, David had always amazed Susan with his timekeeping and time of arrival predictions. Travelling from London to Bristol, he would say that with maybe 180 miles to go, "we will arrive at about ten past three." Sure enough, they would arrive almost to the minute.

David and Jenny walked into the Hotel Reception, and David ushered Jenny toward the bar area.

"Excuse me a minute, I've just got to ask the reception something," David said as he directed Jenny towards the bar area and he went towards the Reception.

Jenny entered the bar area and found a suitable place to sit on a very soft, inviting leather lounger. A minute later, David joined her.

"Gosh, this is very luxurious," exclaimed Jenny casting an eye around the salubrious surroundings.

"It's very pleasant, isn't it? I have been here to celebrate a couple of birthdays, and it always seems to hit the spot," David smiled in reply.

As David was just about to say something, a lady from Reception arrived at the table.

"Miss Dolton?" the lady addressed Jenny.

"Yes," Jenny responded, somewhat surprised that the lady knew her name.

"I wondered if you would like to come this way, please?" the lady requested.

Jenny's surprise turned to bewilderment. David shrugged his shoulders as if to say, sorry, I haven't got a clue. Jenny dutifully followed the lady. Unbeknown to her, David had called ahead and asked if there was a spa treatment available. The spa was fully booked except for a 40-minute facial appointment.

It seemed little more than a short period until Jenny returned smiling from ear to ear.

"Wow, that was a bit of a surprise. Thank you very much." She said as she gave David a peck on the cheek and a warm hug.

"My pleasure. It seemed to me that you were under a bit of stress at the moment and might benefit from a bit of pampering," David smiled warmly in return.

David spoke candidly, "So, where do you want to start? What are your thoughts? I have to say I was extremely flattered by your comments the other day. I have treated tens of thousands of female patients, but I had never felt the chemistry with anyone as I did when you first came in. If I am honest, I should have been more professional from the outset and referred you to another chiropractor. But to be truthful, after the shit I have been through, with my divorce and my ex and the depression that I have suffered, I enjoyed the attention of an attractive woman. But how can you be considering marrying someone if you are so uncertain about how you feel about him?"

"I don't know, I really don't know," she said passively.

"I know they say that you get cold feet when you get close to marriage and even consider a last-minute fling. But is that what you were thinking?" David posed.

"No, not at all. It's just that I have never felt such chemistry and such a connection with someone before. It has been an amazing feeling that I cannot describe," she said, clasping David's hand.

He did not remove his hand but allowed Jenny to hold it and could feel a wonderful energy that he could not recall feeling before with anyone.

"Oh, okay, well, the chemistry is clearly mutual, which I suppose, in order for one person to feel this way, it has to be mutual, hence the phrase chemistry, the reaction between two elements. But it's okay for me, as I am single and have no commitments. So beyond not conflating the professional with the personal, which we have now segregated, I am a free agent. But what about you, Jenny? Where is your head?"

"I don't know, I really don't know," she repeated.

"Well, at the moment, you are programmed to go to Portugal and get married unless you make a proactive decision to change what is due to happen," David reminded her pleasantly but also bluntly.

"But he will go wild. He will go berserk. He is a very aggressive, protective, and jealous guy, the total opposite of you, David. You're soft, gentle, considerate, caring, the total opposite," Jenny outlined.

"Well okay. But the clock is ticking, Jenny. Now we have not known each other for very long, and I may not be the ideal person for you. But what your emotion does seem to show is that you do not have the strength of love to commit to Simon for the rest of your life, do you?" David raised an eyebrow as he finished his question.

"No, I don't think I do, but what can I do?" Her eyes were filling with tears, as she could feel that her warmth of emotions was with David, and yet, in less than 10 days, she was due to be marrying another man.

"Do you love him?" David asked pointedly.

Jenny looked straight into David's eyes and said nothing. Her expression said that she did not want to answer such a direct question.

"Do you love him, Jenny?" David asked again.

She looked at him as if she had not heard the question, still choosing not to respond.

"At the moment, it seems that due to his demeanour, and your fear of what he might do to you, and you not wanting to rock the boat, you are going to go ahead with something that you have realized is not right" David's voice firm but fair. "Am I right?"

Jenny looked like a child wanting her father to solve a difficult problem with a persistent and tenacious but unwanted first boyfriend.

"I can't tell you what to do, Jenny. You have to make the decision. If you want to be with him, then fine, do nothing, and let things flow. But if so, then really, you should not have involved me and my emotions. You knew my recent history, and unless you wished something to happen between us, perhaps you should have shown me some respect and just done your own thing". David said in a slightly harsher tone.

"Hmm, perhaps you're right. But I really was not prepared for the emotion that hit me when I walked into your reception three weeks ago. I thought I was just coming to a chiropractor who would help me deal with my neck pain. How did I know that I was going to feel so strongly for you?" Jenny looked in a mildly pitiful manner.

"No, true. Okay. Well, it's Wednesday today. You travel to Portugal on Sunday, don't you, for the marriage next Thursday – Referendum Day!"

56

Jenny nodded, her head feeling somewhat claustrophobic at the thought that such a momentous day was literally just around the corner, and she was clearly not in the right head space to accept the inevitability that was about to unfold.

David had felt that he had said enough. He had been open and frank enough to let Jenny know that he had felt strong emotions for her but could not do anymore in the short time before she was due to get married.

He chose to change the tone of the conversation whilst they ate their lunch.

The drive back to Silkmoor was quiet, and David sensed that Jenny was in deep thought. Arriving at the clinic, they exited the car, and Jenny walked towards her BMW that she had been able to secrete behind a wall within the curtilage of the clinic.

"Well, okay, so the next time I see you, I imagine that you will be married," David said with an air of resolution.

Jenny smiled very apologetically. She moved forward, kissed David full on the lips, and gave him a long warm hug. "Thank you so much for today."

She opened her car door, fitted her seat belt, and slowly drove away.

Chapter 5 – The Wedding

Seeing Jenny drive away and the emotion evoked, reminded David of the times he had said goodbye to his parents after spending a weekend with them. He had for many years, whilst being an architect, worked in London, whilst his parents lived in the West Country, just a few miles inland from Bude in North Cornwall.

At the end of a weekend, he would reverse his car out of his parents' driveway, and his parents would stand at the junction of the driveway and the access road that led off the main road to their house. For the 200 yards from the driveway until the junction with the main road, he could see them waving in his rearview mirror. His parents would remain at the end of the drive until he was out of sight and onto the main road.

This small but poignant tradition had gone on for years until one fateful day. Due to the decline in work in London, David decided to take the opportunity of working for VSO Voluntary Services Overseas as an architect and was posted to Malawi. At the end of his last weekend in the UK before travelling, he had said his farewells to his parents and was driving down the access road, as he had done numerous times before.

However, this time as he looked in his rearview mirror for the final time, his father was no longer there. David became more than a little perplexed as he felt that, as he was not going to see his father for in excess of two years, the least his father could have done was to stay and wave him off. His perplexity turned to frustration and annoyance the more he allowed himself to consider how inconsiderate his father had been, such that, after a few weeks in Malawi, he felt compelled to mention his dissatisfaction, as to what his father had done, in a letter home. When he received a letter of reply from his mother a month or so after he had left the West Country, the words in the letter conveyed a totally different version of how David had perceived the event.

Jack Roseman was a self-made businessman who, in his 60-plus years, of running his own construction company, and employing in excess of 30 men full-time across all the trades, was a very reserved man. David had only known a very strict, authoritarian father. Someone who would resort to corporal punishment at the drop of a hat. The only time that David had seen a softer side of his father was after David had fractured his ankle as an eighteen-year-old whilst playing football for one of the local teams in the league that his father happened to be chairman. His father turned instantly into the most caring and considerate mother hen that anyone could wish them to be.

David's mother explained that after she had seen the car disappear from view, she had walked back into the house, expecting to see Jack sitting in front of the television in the lounge. Not being there, she went into the kitchen, ostensibly to make a cup of tea. But as she opened the kitchen door, she saw her husband sitting in his chair by the kitchen table, his head buried in his hands and, as she wrote, "crying like a baby."

"Why has he got to go all the way to Africa to find work? What is wrong with my business? What have I done to deserve this?" Jack said forlornly and with tears streaming down his cheeks.

Such a gentle underbelly to his father's emotions David had never experienced in his 30 years of being his son. It would be over two years now before he could show his father how much that love, that he never knew existed, had meant to him.

The week following their visit to Blunton Lodge passed off as any other. David was busy with patients in the clinic and had enjoyed a fun cricket match playing for the Overoptomists on the Wednesday evening, and following his son's cricket fortunes at the weekend with his school team.

Jenny's Wedding was set to take place at 1.00p.m local time in Portugal on Thursday, 21st June, also Referendum Day, when the UK was due to vote on whether to stay in the European Union. How ironic was that, David thought.

As he had done since the break up of his marriage, David woke up early on that Thursday. He went into the lounge, put on the television, and, as was often the case, listened to a hard-hitting Stephen Sacker interview of some third-world politician being torn apart on Hard Talk.

At about 7.30 am, the messenger on his phone binged. It was from Jenny.

"Hi, how are you xxx?"

With a mixture of surprise and delight, David noticed the three "xxx's" in the text. Jenny had never been so expressive as to sign a text with three kisses before. He responded with trepidation, "I'm fine, but what about you, more importantly?' What are you doing? How are you feeling xx?"

"Well, I'm here, just having my breakfast in bed and waiting for the hair stylist to arrive xxx."

Again the three kisses, which reassured David that the first was not done in error, which could have been the case, if she had just messaged a close friend, or family member just before sending David a message.

"Are you happy with how you are feeling xxx?" David asked tentatively, adding an extra kiss, as if to add some gravitas to his feelings towards her.

"I really do not know whether I am doing the right thing, I'm here, and it's lovely, and my family from Ireland have arrived, but I am not sure if I am just going along with the flow."

What was she saying? Did she want direction? Did she want David to tell her not to go ahead? What should he do, he thought? Should he be stoic and British and the supportive stiff upper-lipped gent? Or should he pour out his heart? But how cruel would that be to do that to a woman so far away, a mere few hours from such a momentous part of her life?

"I really do not know what you want me to say, Jenny. Do you want me to tell you what to do, even though I am not there and do not know where the truth is with your emotions xxx?"

"I feel lost and alone xxx," she texted.

"Well, doesn't that tell you all you need to know? You're with your friends and family and fiancée, all there, close to you, supporting you, and you feel lost and alone? Surely, if your emotions were in the right place, you would be feeling elated, relaxed, if a little nervous, yes, but contented and excited to start a new part of your life".

"Hmm, yes, you're right, but I don't think I do xxx."

"Okay, well, that is not necessarily a problem if you, therefore, choose to walk away before the ceremony. Xxx"

"I've got to go. I'm sorry, my relatives are at the door. I'll speak to you later, darling xxx."

With that, the screen went blank, and David was left to prepare for his morning clinic. Luckily, he had volunteered to play cricket against a touring side in the afternoon, so he only had to concentrate from the morning until lunchtime.

But what was going on? Was he being played? Was this woman just getting high by realizing that she had the interest of two guys and enjoying the attention? Or did she genuinely feel something for David but felt trapped to go through with the marriage? Was she scared of her fiancée?

Was he as aggressive, possessive, and unpleasant as she had portrayed him to be? The only interaction that David had had with Simon in the pub illustrated that, at best, he was not blessed with social graces. He had an air of thinking that he was someone and that others should show him respect, when in fact, he was just an insipid man with an inflated ego.

The clinic went well as David was lucky to have a full morning list, which made him concentrate on his patients, and not have time to try and work out what was going on in Portugal.

The cricket match started at 2.00 pm., on a very warm, cloudless, windless afternoon. The touring team had come up from Newbury and had done so for the last 12-15 years.

Silkmoor had put together a mixture of first-team players from their club, together with the captain and groundsman from the club 50 yards down the road, players from the second team, third team, and a couple from David's side, the Overoptomists.

In the team was Silkmoor's overseas player from Australia. A young, fast left-arm bowler who was following a long line of young Australians who had come over during the summer months to experience playing in England. Often these players ended up representing Australia at first-class levels a little later in their careers.

David had been a wicketkeeper since his prep school days. His speed of hands and surety of catching, added to his total inability to be able to bowl at all, made him the ideal candidate to keep wicket in his school days.

Silkmoor chose to bat and made a reasonable start. At 156 for 3, David walked to the wicket. Not known for his shot-making, he had, in the last year, attempted to improve his batting by getting one-to-one lessons with a Sri Lankan coach, whose international cricketing career had come to an unfortunate end when, whilst representing his national side at under 16 levels, he had attempted to take a catch on the boundary. But due to having to run around the boundary in an attempt to take the ball, was only able to offer one hand for the catch. Somehow instead of hitting his palm, the ball had landed directly between his third and fourth fingers, with such a force as to split his palm from the junction of the fourth finger towards his wrist, ending a very promising career.

Off the third ball faced, David struck a cover drive for four, and his innings had commenced. However, sadly three balls later, he missed a ball, pitched outside his off stump, and whilst he was reviewing what had gone wrong in his mind and replayed the shot, he had inadvertently forgotten to make his ground, and the wicketkeeper standing back, had thrown the ball at the wicket and ran David out.

Sitting out the remaining overs caused him to contemplate what was happening currently, what had happened in Portugal this morning, and what might be occurring now. As he had not had a message of desperation, he had assumed that Jenny had gone through with the marriage.

David's position in this ad hoc cricket team was as a wicketkeeper. Each inning lasted for 30 overs and, in the June sun, tested his fitness somewhat. As a young man, the persistent crouching and standing, ball after ball, had, had no ill effect on him. In fact, muscularly, it did not have any detrimental effect that day either. However, as one ages, the efficiency of the body reduces somewhat. One of the main aims of the heart is to maintain the blood pressure constant within the body. Clearly, the pressure will alter, and the resistance will change in the arteries, depending on the position of the body. Lying down, there is no gravity to work against, and therefore, the heart rate can be less, to maintain even pressure than when one is stood up, and the effect of gravity causes a slight increase in heart rate to maintain the optimal pressure. Clearly, the critical organ in regards to consistent blood pressure, and therefore continuous supply, is the brain. Any temporary loss of pressure, and thus supply, will starve the brain of the oxygen it needs, and therefore cause someone to feel faint, if not actually to faint. To ensure continuity of pressure, dependent on posture, there are sensors within the carotid arteries in the neck that relay an electrical signal directly to the heart, to either increase or decrease the heart rate. Of course, when one is crouching and standing persistently, these monitors are firing off all the time.

With age, the efficiency of the relay system reduces. This is why it is common for older people who wake up at night to go to the toilet to feel a little dizzy, if they move from lying to standing too quickly. David felt the same effect whilst keeping wicket, which was heightened as the afternoon went on, and he became more dehydrated by the sunny weather.

After ten overs of relative pace, the first change bowlers came on. Sebastian, who was standing at first slip and of a similar age to David, but who had played a lot of senior cricket as a batsman, leaned across and said, "I think you might need to stand back another yard for this lad David," smiling knowingly.

"Why he's a first-change bowler and only about 19?" David said with surprise.

"Yes, I know, but he is an Australian professional, and he has already played some Sheffield Shield cricket before he came here," Sebastian said calmly. Sheffield Shield was a similar level of cricket in Australia to county cricket in England.

Begrudgingly David stepped back another yard. The Australian came in and instantly produced a ball a good 10 miles an hour quicker than anything that had been bowled already. Consequently, the pace beat the batsmen, and the ball thudded into David's gloves. Even with inners and good quality leather gloves, the moment of impact hurt his palms. Ball after ball, the batsmen played and missed, and David fielded the ball. The sensation of his hands was unique to anything he had experienced in 30 years of keeping. His mind focused not only on concentrating on keeping competently against this bowler, but also on the concern as to how his hands might be in order to be able to treat his patients the next day. Inside the gloves, they felt black and blue. The benefit of the experience was that all thoughts of Portugal were wiped from his mind.

The match ended with a 30-run victory to Silkmoor. Gentlemanly congratulations ensued between the members of both teams, and beer and a barbeque brought a satisfactory end to a quintessential English summer's afternoon.

Five hours in the sun and a few beers ensured that David did not suffer the same fate as the evening before, with his mind cogitating the ifs and buts of the goings on in Portugal. A hot bath, a glass of wine, and an early retirement to bed, resulted in almost instant rapid eye movement, and deep sleep, as he reflected on wicketkeeping to someone bowling at over 80 mph.

The next week passed with little commentary, beyond a busy period in the clinic and satisfied patients leaving, following successful treatment.

The morning of Monday 4th July was similar to many before until, at about 11.30 a.m. David received a text from Jenny.

"Hi, how are you? Xxx," she wrote.

Still, three kisses. So, had she got married, or had she taken time out and was contacting him on her return to the UK? If she had got married, why would she contact him on her first day back, after returning home from the honeymoon that weekend? Clearly, it would probably be the first time that she was not with Simon, and one might have assumed that he would have gone back to work. But why would a happily married woman contact a guy who she knew had had an interest in her, directly on her return from honeymoon? If nothing else, it seemed somewhat callous, if not a little cruel.

Gingerly David responded, "I'm fine, thank you. How are you?"

Strangely, David did not want to ask the obvious question as to how the wedding went, because if he did, then he would most likely hear that it was fine, or it was great, and either way, he would know that she had gone through with it and that would be the end of it.

"What are you doing now?" came the reply.

"I'm between patients in the clinic. I've had a cancellation. Why?' he asked tentatively. Again he thought, why would she ask? Why was she trying to make polite conversation? Hadn't the actions that happened ten days before closed the door on their situation, however much their friendship had been in its infancy?

"Oh, ok. Well, as you know, I started my induction at LGI today, and it was meant to go on all day, but it's finished already. I was just wondering if you would like to meet for lunch?" Jenny texted back.

What was she doing to him? Was she deliberately playing with his mind, or was she just a lifelong prick tease?

"Well, I have no plans, so we could meet if you wish. Where are you now?' he texted, perplexed and excited, in equal measure.

"I'm just walking to the train station to get the train back to Burton. So ,once I have picked up my car, I could meet you at the Bull and Baby in about forty-five minutes".

"Yes, of course, that would be great, thank you." Why had he said thank you? What was he thanking her for? His mind was even more confused than it had been when they said goodbye a fortnight ago after lunch at Blunton Lodge.

Forty minutes later, David was driving up the main moor road, out of Silkmoor, to the landmark pub opposite the famous Bull and Baby that overlooked the town. As he reversed his car into the space, Jenny pulled in a couple of cars away in the car park. He walked towards her and noticed that she was wearing a short summer skirt and a light blouse: not ideal for a walk on Silkmoor Moor, on a day with a stiff breeze around, which was nearly every day up there.

As they got close, David angled his head to give Jenny a peck on the cheek, but before he was able to maneuver himself to kiss her cheek, she had planted a very succulent kiss directly on his lips. At the same time, she took his hand and gesticulated towards the moor.

"I think it's better if we go for a walk instead of going in the pub as I do not know who we might meet in there," she said as she strode off hand in hand with David.

The most obvious thing to ask someone who had just come back from a honeymoon was how it was. But then again, it was not the most obvious thing for someone who had just come back from honeymoon to be calling someone who she knew fancied her, to arrange to meet for lunch, and then plant a very deliberate kiss on his lips, and then walks hand in hand, with him up to the Bull and Baby rocks.

Had he been in a stronger state of mind, David would not have entertained the meet, let alone be happy to be hand in hand with a woman who he believed had just become betrothed to another man, ten days earlier. But as had occurred right from their first meet, due to the psychological trauma resulting from the fallout of his marriage, David was desperate for physical warmth and emotional attention.

They walked towards the top of the Bull and Baby in the gusting wind.

"Let's get on top of the Bull," she said.

It was clear to David exactly what was going to happen to someone wearing a short skirt on a hill, in the gusting wind, attempting to take a step, two feet in the air, to get onto a rock. And sure enough, as Jenny attempted to climb onto the rock, the wind got under her skirt, and for much longer than one would expect a lady to allow to occur, David was treated to a full frontal of her skimpy underwear.

As she had done when the gown had slipped in the treatment room to expose her right breast, Jenny appeared totally non-plussed at exposing her underwear to David.

"So, how was the first day of initiation at LGI," David asked, so as not to mention the elephant in the room.

"Good, thank you, yes, good. Although it is a long time since I trained, and there are a lot of much younger occupational therapists there, who seem to have a different philosophy to me, that I am not sure if I am going to fit in."

"Well, you can suck it and see, and if not, I presume that you can go more into the private sector, or do more community work. Talking of which, I have a couple of friends who are GPs who I play cricket, and I was asking them if they have an in-house Occupational Health section. They said that they hadn't, so if it does not work at LGI, you might consider introducing yourself to them".

"Yes, that sounds like a good idea. But I wouldn't want to work from home though," she said, sounding slightly deflated that the lack of suitable premises could mean losing the opportunity of working with a large surgery.

"Well, I have a spare treatment room, of course, if you think that might be useful."

"Oh yes, of course. Hmm, now there's an idea," she said, smiling knowingly from ear to ear.

They both stood side by side, hand in hand, in silence for a minute or two, looking across Silkmoor to Skippingdale and the Dales beyond.

Chapter 6 – What to Do!

Returning to the clinic, David had many more questions than answers. Clearly, Jenny's statement during lunch at Blunton Lodge, that she would know if she loved Simon the moment she walked down the aisle, if somewhat last minute, did not seem, if her recent actions, since her return from honeymoon had been genuine, to have become manifest.

Of course, despite the intensity of emotions that had been projected between the two of them, the length of time that they had actually known each other, was still not much more than five weeks. How could one understand the mind of someone in five weeks? More things are still to be found out than have become known in such time.

Perhaps Jenny was a woman who just loved the attention and playing on men's emotions. Perhaps she enjoyed the excitement of the chase, as well as the security of a defined home life. Perhaps she now had all that she needed, a man to look after her at home, and another who she could toy with and tease and tempt emotionally, for her own gratification and titillation.

The rest of the week passed without anymore communication other than a "good morning" text and a "have a nice day" and "how was your day" message.

On 12th July, Jenny texted David at around 8.00 a.m. in the morning. She had gone to the station to find that her train had been cancelled, due to a fallen tree on the line. She stated that she had not got her house keys, as she had left them inside the house, as when she was due to come home in the evening, Simon would already be there, so she had not felt the need to take them. She wondered if David could pick her up from Burton station and bring her back to Silkmoor, so that she could stay at his flat until the line had cleared.

Confused as to why she did not contact her husband, but also happy to oblige, David drove the four miles to Burton and picked her up from the station. They drove back to Silkmoor, making pleasantries after Jenny had thanked him for coming to her asistance. David directed her to make herself at home upstairs whilst he did his clinic. An hour later, the line was clear. Jenny said her thank you's and caught the train from Silkmoor station.

Throughout the following six weeks, Jenny and David met quite frequently, either for the train journey home from Leeds, or directly after work for a quick drink. Their friendship blossomed, and the warmth and connection intensified; yet there was no intimacy beyond hugs and cursory kisses on the cheeks.

They seemed to be running a relationship in a somewhat parallel universe to part of the rest of her life. Both of them knew that she was married, but the subject was never brokered. David had assumed that Jenny had gone through with the marriage because she was too afraid not too. But she had decided that she could have open emotions with another man, as long as she did not sleep with that other man. She seemed to want to spend all her available spare time with David instead of her new husband. They met for coffee, frequent lunches, at the golf driving range, where David helped Jenny improve her golf swing; drinks after work in Leeds, and Jenny even came by the clinic after her visits to her private patients and used David's computer in the clinic, to write up the paperwork that could have been done much easier at her home, but which afforded her more time with David.

So, nine weeks after her marriage it would appear that, emotionally, it was a marriage of convenience, and that there was no depth of emotion, or love between Jenny and her husband.

Mid to late afternoon on Friday, 26th August, Jenny unusually called David's phone instead of texting him.

"Hi, are you busy in the clinic at the moment?" she said in a slightly clipped and agitated tone.

"I have three more treatments, and then I am done for the weekend. Why?" David asked, concerned as to Jenny's level of agitation.

"What time will you finish?" she asked, clearly wanting to see him.

"I will be done by 4.40," David responded.

"Can you meet me please, after 4.40?" her voice, somewhat desperate now.

"I have Daniel this weekend, and he is here now. But I could meet you for half an hour or so if it was near by," David replied, a little concerned as to why she was desperate to see him, and appeared a little agitated.

"I'm going to take the dog for a walk, so could you meet me for a walk, please?" her voice pleading.

"Yes, sure. Where would you like to meet?" David replied.

"Well, there is a lay-by on the Silkmoor side of Burton, just beyond the last speed bump. If you meet me there, we can go for a walk up on the moor."

"Ok, but your car will be prominent there and easy to be viewed by anyone passing," David said, thinking that it might be a route that Simon took on his way home.

"Oh, don't worry, he's gone to Bradford for a haircut, so won't be back for over an hour," she said in a manner that appeared that she had things planned out.

In all the time that David had known Jenny, she rarely called her husband by his name. She often did not refer to him at all, but when she did, it was always as "he". It was also said with little affection or warmth, which was more emphasized, particularly as they had only been married nine weeks.

It was a warm, if somewhat breezy, late afternoon when they met in the lay-by. Jenny had already taken the dog out of the car and was making as if to walk over the style to get onto the moor. But in fact, she was loitering until David arrived. As soon as he got out of his car, she walked onto the moor to ensure that anyone in a car passing by, would think that they were two independent people who had just happened to arrive for a walk, at almost the same time, but were not together.

Once they were both on the moor and less obvious to passing traffic, she stopped to allow David to catch her up.

It was clear that Jenny did not want to be seen giving or receiving a kiss from David, so he brushed his hand along her upper arm and forearm in an expression of warmth.

"So what's wrong? You sounded perplexed and agitated on the phone?" David asked.

She stopped, turned directly to face David, and said with deep concern in her voice,

"I have made the worst decision of my life. I can't tell you!"

There was a strong part of David that wanted to say, "I told you so," or "it was obvious, weeks before the marriage, that something was not right". Instead, he smiled warmly and asked what particularly had happened.

It transpired that the Saturday before, she and Simon had gone out for the evening with their next-door neighbours, who had also been at the wedding. The man had been one of the ushers at the wedding. Not long after they had finished their first pint, Simon had turned somewhat aggressive towards the man, and asked him why he had posted photos of the wedding on his Facebook page. The guy had looked bemused and somewhat offended and responded in a way as to say, why would he not post photos of the wedding in such a fashion? He had been at the wedding and naturally taken photos, and as Facebook was a medium on which people posted photos of their life experiences, why would he not have posted such photos? In many ways, it could be seen as an affront to the newly married couple if they had not posted the photos on their Facebook page!

The evening worsened the more that Simon drank, and before long, he had taken a verbal broadside at Jenny's daughters, who had had a turbulent relationship with him throughout all the time that Jenny had been with him. At one point, Simon had said of Jenny's eldest. "If she were mine, I'd rip her fucking head off, no word of a lie!"

"Hmm, well, that's not exactly what I would expect a step-father to say at any stage, but particularly after just a few weeks of becoming betrothed to their mother. I have sensed that he is more than a bit aggressive, but why would he have an issue with your children? That's beyond the pale!" David said, whilst motioning the dog to pick up the stick it had dropped at David's feet.

"And we are due to be going off to the Belfry this bank holiday weekend for golf and golf tuition," she said with uncertainly.

The Belfry is a very prestigious golf complex in the Midlands that had hosted the Ryder Cup a few times in the 1980s. David had played on one of the courses when he attended a Chiropractic Conference to celebrate the 75th Anniversary of the English Chiropractic Association.

"Ah, ok, well, do you still want to go?" David enquired.

"Well, I don't think that I have a choice!" Jenny answered.

"Well, you do. We all do!" David responded somewhat more forcibly.

"I'll be okay. I can focus on the golf, I suppose," she said, somewhat resigned not to having the nicest of weekends.

"Well, if there is any issue, and you want to leave early, then you can always get a train back and stay over at the flat if it helps. I have two spare bedrooms," David offered, in an attempt to give her an option, should things turn out sour.

"Thank you, David, that's very considerate" Jenny grasped his arm and squeezed in recognition of the gesture.

By this time in their conversation, they had returned off the moor and quickly said their goodbyes. As he drove off, David wound his window down and said, "If you need any help, just let me know".

Jenny smiled as she closed the boot and sat in her car, ready to drive off. Before she did, she sat and thought of the events of the last three months, and how clear things were, and how much of a bad decision she had made.

She drove back to her house, contemplating whether she should feign some excuse not to go to the Belfry. Could she tolerate spending the whole weekend with the man who, the night before, had stated that he wished to rip her daughter's head off?

David heard nothing more from Jenny on Friday night, or throughout Saturday. He and Daniel had gone to the cricket nets to practice Daniel's batting. Daniel was 12 and loved cricket. He had become a wicketkeeper for his school team, mostly to follow in his dad's footsteps. Ironically though, even though he stood behind the stumps to field all the balls bowled to him, he was nervous about facing balls bowled to him when he was batting. They regularly went to the nets at Silkmoor Cricket Club, where David would spend an hour doing throw downs to help Daniel's timing of hitting the ball with his bat.

Early on Sunday morning, David's phone rang. It was Jenny. On Friday afternoon, she sounded agitated. This time she sounded fearful and distraught.

"He knows about us, he knows about us, and he's furious and mad and uncontrollable. I don't know what to do!" she said in a very emotional and desperate voice,

"Wow, wow, wow, what do you mean – "he knows about us", what us? There is no "us"! What's happened, Jenny?"

"He's found the thread of texts between us on my phone. He's read everything. What am I going to do?" her voice became croaky and high-pitched.

"How did that happen, and what has he found?" David replied in a considered fashion.

It transpired that on the Saturday evening, before getting ready for dinner, Jenny had gone alone for a swim at the hotel pool and left her mobile phone in the bedroom. Being a very suspicious character, Simon had looked through her phone and come across a number of text messages between Jenny and David.

Despite Jenny having found Simon looking through her belongings in her handbag and phone some twelve months earlier, and being aware of his possessive and jealous nature, she had chosen not to put a security code on her phone, thus enabling anyone to just access anything on it.

For someone who was so afraid of the aggression possessed by her husband, who also knew how he would react, should he become aware that his wife had a friendship with another man, let alone was texting him, it did seem more than a little odd, that she had not applied, even the basic security to her phone, to stop her husband searching through it.

A clinical psychologist who was cognizant of the nature of her relationship with her husband and her current emotions surrounding the marriage might conclude that, either consciously or subconsciously, she had deliberately put herself in jeopardy so that the events would unfold as they naturally would. Thus, perhaps deliberately scuppering the marriage, by the mere fact that Simon would say that she had been unfaithful and look to end the marriage, and hence give her an out clause.

"So, what's happening now?" David asked furtively.

"We're coming home today, and he has told me to come and stay with you. There was almost a fight in the bar last night. They had to call security to stop him from attacking me. I wanted to stay in another room, but being that it was a bank holiday, they were fully booked, and we had to share the same room," she explained.

"Wow, that couldn't have been easy," he replied. Nor will the trip home be David thought. Rather them than me. They would not be comparing golf swings, that was for sure.

Three hours later, there was a knock at the front door of David's house, and when he peered out of the kitchen window, on the floor directly above the entrance, Jenny was standing there with her suitcase in hand. Simon had decided to make a melodramatic scene of her texting David, and rather than drive them both home, had driven directly to David's clinic and forced her out of the car, before driving off, acting like an agitated eighteen-year-old putting his new one-litre engine car to the floor at a set of traffic lights, in a vane attempt to burn off a three-litre sports car sat in the adjacent lane.

David opened the door, and Jenny fell into his arms, trembling and half crying. He invited her upstairs to the flat, sat her down, made a coffee, and the post-mortem commenced.

An hour later, Jenny was no clearer as to what she wanted to do in relation to her marriage; work the next day, or even where she wanted to stay that night. David had offered her the spare room, but she was fearful that if she stayed, Simon would get the wrong end of the stick, and that would make things worse.

Once she had calmed down, she decided that the best thing was to go home, sleep in the spare room, and consider her future, once he had gone to work the next day. David gave her a reassuring hug as she left the clinic, telling her to keep in touch and come back should things become unsafe.

David called a taxi and waved goodbye to Jenny as the taxi moved away. Jenny was more nervous than she had ever been in her life before. What would happen when she turned the key? Would Simon be there, or would he have gone out to drown his sorrows in the local pub?

When she arrived, his car was there, but she knew as soon as she entered the house that he was not in. She went upstairs, got undressed, and moved all her toiletries from the ensuite in the master bedroom, into the bathroom directly next to the spare room. She went into the spare bedroom and locked the door behind her.

The minutes seemed to take an eternity to pass as she nervously waited to hear the front door open. She must have eventually fallen asleep, as the next thing she heard was the handle of the door of her locked bedroom twist. It twisted again, but beyond the slight sound of the handle turning, there was no other noise.

She heard the main door to the bedroom slam and, a few moments later, the audio from the television in the bedroom. She froze in bed, not knowing what to do, but desperately hoping that she would get off to sleep quickly.

Six hours later, she was still wishing that she could fall asleep. She had thought through almost every moment from their first meeting. Why had she missed the obvious signs of his possessive, aggressive, jealous personality? Why had she not seen the time that he had pinned her up against the wall and accused her of sleeping with the next-door neighbour, just because he had seen her talking to him across the garden fence, as a sign that this man was not normal?

Why had she not taken the emotions that she had felt when she had first met David as an indication of what a decent, kind, chivalrous man could be like?

The next morning she woke, not knowing how long she had slept or if she was in the house alone. From memory, Simon had a meeting on-site with a plasterer, who was coming to give him a quote to skim the inside of a house they were renovating. The house had been bought by Jenny with her own money about a year before the marriage. Simon, however, had chosen to set himself up as a developer and had taken over the management of the alterations to the property. In order to be able to transport materials to the site, he had, unbeknown to Jenny, sold her car so that he could purchase a van. Such an authoritarian act had annoyed her, as it reduced her independence, but she chose not to make an issue of it.

It was now 8.27 a.m., and she was sure that the meeting had been arranged for 8.30 a.m. on site. She lay still, trying to listen to hear any movement in the rest of the house. Once she had convinced herself that no one else was in the house, she got up, unlocked the door, and tentatively walked across the landing to the bathroom. The same landing that, not more than nine weeks earlier, she had been carried across by her new groom, as he took her into their marital bedroom for the first time, on their return from honeymoon. The house was calm, and Jenny sighed as she prepared herself for the day ahead.

Four days after Jenny had turned up on his doorstep in distress, David's clinic morning was unspectacular, with patients from 7.00 a.m., every 20 minutes. The vast majority of patients reported improvements in their conditions from the last treatment, which was always a pleasant situation.

The clinic phone rang just before 11.00 a.m. It was Jenny, her voice was agitated, and she sounded very anxious.

"Can you talk?" she asked tentatively.

"Yes, no problem. I have had a cancellation, so we can chat for 10 minutes or so. What's wrong? You sound very anxious?" David asked with a degree of concern.

"He's going to do you in. He says that you need to be taught a lesson. He has a gun at the house, and he's part of the Mafia. So you must take care. You must be cautious." Jenny explained, still somewhat anxiously, but calmer than her initial statement.

"Wow, wow, wow, he's part of the Mafia, and he owns a gun! What do you mean he's part of the Mafia?" David asked with concern and some disbelief that someone who lived in a small village in West Yorkshire had contact with the Mafia, let alone was a member. He had not heard of any Mafiosi activity in the Leeds or Bradford area, so what was she saying?

"He's told me that he's part of the Mafia and therefore has connections and is going to have you done in. He's not going to dirty his hands, he says, but he knows someone who will do it for him," Jenny stated much more calmly and lucidly than before.

"And knowing him as you do, do you believe him, or is it just bravado, based on hurt and a damaged machismo?" David asked.

"Well, he's very angry and aggressive. I've never seen him like this before. You need to contact the Police and tell them that he is out to get you," she directed.

"Wow, wait a minute, what are you doing now? Why don't you contact the Police on your and my behalf? After all, you may also be at risk, might you not?" David's voice was becoming a little frustrated.

How had he become embroiled, in a marital situation, without any input, beyond emotional support, to such an extent that a patient's husband was saying that he was going to put out a contract on him.

"I'm on my way to a golf lesson now, so I can't do it," Jenny replied.

Flabbergasted, aghast, and in total disbelief as to what he had just heard.

"Sorry Jenny, you have just told me that you have a concern, that your aggressive, jealous, nutty husband is going to have me done in, and yet you have the composure to go and have a golf lesson? Do you not think that you have got your priorities somewhat confused here? What am I going to say when I contact the Police? Sorry Officer, I have been contacted by one of my ex patients today, who says that because her husband found some innocuous messages from me on her phone, he is going to contact some friends in the mafia, who are going to come and have me done in! What do you think they

83

are going to say? They are going to ask what evidence I have to substantiate this, and all I will be able to say is that a patient of mine has just rung and told me this fact, as she was driving on her way to her golf lesson! No, you are the concerned person, and respectfully, you are also the person who witnessed your husband's statements and saw how angry he was, so whoever it may be, who the person who may be injured is, because you heard the proposed action that your husband intends to evoke, it is YOUR duty of care towards me, and it is YOU who must contact the Police and outline the exact situation immediately. For fuck sake Jenny, get a grip, and get your priorities right. Who on earth would consider going for a fucking golf lesson first?"

"Oh ok, leave it with me," she said meekly.

"Right, I am going to ring off now, and I need you to text, or call me when you have spoken to the Police and tell me what they have said." He put the phone down immediately at the end of his sentence without any chance of receiving a response.

Once he had taken a few minutes to calm down, and consider how selfish someone could be, to involve a third party in a family dispute, and not have the due grace to contact the Police, but prefer to continue with a golf lesson instead, he decided to contact the Police anyway. How could he trust someone whose respect for others was that obtuse?

The call to the Police did not last long. The Police understood the predicament and said that they would happily look into the situation regarding firearms and any known connection with the Mafia.

At 3.20 pm. on the same day, the clinic door opened unexpectedly. David did not have another patient until 3.40 p.m. Two police constables presented themselves and stated that they were responding to a telephone call received from Mrs. Rossington. David ushered them into his treatment room, and the two officers said down. One officer, who was clearly the most senior, was in his mid 30's, and the junior officer in his early 20s.

"Hello, Dr. Roseman. Further to receiving a telephone call from Mrs. Rossington this morning, we have had reason to investigate Mr. Rossington, due to the nature of the concerns that she expressed. We are aware that he has a small firearm under licence, but we have absolutely no evidence that he has any connections with the Mafia. We understand that he may be a little bit of a hot head, and of course, we cannot say that he may not come over here and attempt to thump you, but we do not believe that he would be unduly violent". PC Owen Morgan stated.

"Well, first, thank you for being expeditious and investigating the concerns. It is not very pleasant to believe that one might be subject to a violent act, particularly as all I have been doing is offering this lady a shoulder and some lay counseling, in effect." David smiled and started to relax.

After a few pleasantries and the officers stating that if anything violent or out of the ordinary did occur, to contact the Police immediately, both officers left, and David prepared himself for his next patient.

Later in the afternoon, David's mobile rang. It was Jenny.

"I've spoken to the Police," she said in a manner that sounded as if she wanted to be congratulated for what she had done.

"Yes, I know. They have been here and said that he doesn't have any Mafia connections. So, what the hell is going on, Jenny?" David's anger being very apparent in his voice.

"Listen, he's gone through my phone, and he has accessed my Facebook page. He says he wants all your text messages. He wants me to get a copy of all your texts. You must erase all the text. Make sure you do it as soon as you can". Her voice was very agitated.

"Wow, Jenny, he may be your husband, but from my perspective, he is an absolute arse who is creating needless and unjustifiable stress for both you and me. Now he may be able to pressurize you, scare, and bully you, and that is your prerogative, as his wife and partner, to accept the situation. But if you really think that I am going to be directed to do anything because your fucking idiot of a husband demands it, then both you and he have another thing coming. You clearly had an issue with your relationship prior to getting married. I know it, you know it, and most of your relatives know it. You would not have stated that you had an interest in me after three meetings, when you were engaged to be married, if all was perfect with Simon. So, let's be absolutely clear, I have no responsibility to your husband in any way, shape, or fashion. Similarly, in fact, I have no responsibility towards you, as I have discharged you as a patient. But, just because we got on and there was a clear affinity, I have tried to help you. So please do not involve me in your life, and please do not think that I am a subservient character who is going to be dictated to by your fucking prat of a husband," David explained forcibly.

The line on the other end went dead.

Chapter 7 – The Police

Friday, 22nd July 2016, heralded a reasonably busy day in the clinic. Relatively, the overall clinic numbers had been much reduced since the divorce. Prior to the marriage breakup, the clinic would regularly see 130-140 patients per week, with David seeing the majority, between 80-90. Since the divorce, and Susan leaving to set up her own clinic, not more than 300 yards away, the overall numbers had gone down. In the past, it would not have been uncommon for David to see 28-30 patients on a Friday. Now 15-20 was more common.

Since the clinic had reduced from six clinicians to just one, there had been no financial need to retain a practice manager and receptionist. Thus, there was a considerable financial saying in not having to generate an income to pay a practice manager.

Mrs. Brook walked into the Reception from the treatment room and stood by the reception desk. Similar to the desks in the treatment rooms, the reception desk had been designed by David in such a fashion as to allow patients a convenient space to write a cheque, or details of their next appointment, without having to bend down unduly, and therefore affect negatively the treatment that had just been undertaken.

"So, we need to see you early next week, Mrs. Brook. When would be best for you?" David asked kindly whilst bringing up the clinic diary on the computer.

Before Mrs. Brook could respond, the clinic entrance door opened, and a policeman wearing a yellow over jacket and helmet walked very meaningfully into the reception.

"I am looking for Dr. David Roseman," the policeman blurted out forcefully, without any consideration for the process ongoing at the Reception Desk, causing David to look at him in a very dismissive manner.

"I will be with you shortly," David responded in a clear tone of disdain.

"So would Tuesday morning at 9.00 be okay, Mrs. Brook?" David smiled.

"Yes, that would work well, thank you." Mrs. Brook smiled back.

Mrs. Brook paid, said her farewells, and walked tentatively passed the policeman, who had deliberately stood with his hands within his belt, ensuring that he looked as broad and menacing as possible, with his elbows projected lateral to his body, in the middle of the narrow waiting area.

"Now, officer, how can I help you," David said, attempting to hold back how livid he was at the manner that the policeman had needlessly made a totally unwarranted entrance into the clinic.

"You're David Roseman, are you?" the policeman demanded in a harsh, aggressive tone.

"Yes, I am," David said, as he came from behind the Reception Desk and walked towards the officer, who was still standing in a very aggressive manner, in the waiting area.

"Sorry, I thought that you had established that prior to entering my clinic in such an aggressive and insensitive manner, officer." David, now almost face to face with the officer. "Officer Oliver," David said, now being close enough to read the policeman's name. "What's the issue, officer?"

David rarely had any run-ins with the police and was very considerate and respectful of the difficult job that they often had to undertake. But he had taken an immediate dislike to the inconsiderate and disruptive manner in that PC Oliver had stormed into his clinic, to the detrimental effect of him and one of his patients.

"Is there somewhere we can go not to be overheard?" PC Oliver asked, in a slightly softer tone, clearly picking up on David's displeasure.

David ushered the officer into the back room, which had been Susan's treatment room before she had moved out. It had now become Daniel's "snug," where he could take his friends to play on the Xbox and watch movies on Netflix and YouTube.

In the very short time that they had walked the few metres from the reception to the back room, David had felt a certain amount of trepidation. His initial reaction to the officer had been anger, that someone should come into his space, showing absolutely no respect at all. That fight-flight response had now subsided, and he found himself becoming somewhat nervous as to why a police officer would be attending his clinic in such a manner. It could not be due to some very unfortunate news regarding the children, as the officer would have entered in a much meeker manner.

"Mr. Roseman, Mrs. Rossington has attended the police station in Kelbrook and reported that you have been harassing her."

The shock on David's face was clear and obvious. He became perplexed, frustrated, and dismayed as he considered the actions that Jenny had undertaken. She had chosen to present to a police station and fabricate some sort of story, which the police had taken so seriously, as to direct an officer to attend in person.

"Really, and what did Mrs. Rossington say to substantiate such a ridiculous statement?" the shock now subsiding, David could feel his anger rising again.

How could someone who had put him in such a position, in relation to her relationship with her husband, and who had happily received the kindness of his friendship, choose to shaft him, and not only that, to involve the police by fabricating a story of harassment?

"She said that you had been contacting her constantly, despite her telling you not to do so. She said that the pressure that you were putting on her was putting her marriage in jeopardy and that she was fearful of how her husband might react, and did not want to lose him. Therefore, I have here a harassment warning". The officer produced an A4 typed form from inside the jacket of his uniform and gave it to David to read.

On the form, there was a typed statement where Jenny Rossington made certain allegations as to the actions of David. Initially, David scanned the statement rapidly, attempting to comprehend the intent. His anger not allowing him to read the statement so that he could understand it all.

"I need you to sign at the bottom to prove that you accept this, Mr. Roseman," PC Oliver demanded after a short interval.

"I am not going to sign it. What am I signing it for? I do not accept responsibility for these false allegations, and I am definitely not going to condone it by attaching my signature to it." David responded, clearly getting more agitated.

"Well, if you do not sign it, Sir, I will have no choice but to arrest you," PC Oliver stated, getting more forceful in his tone.

"Arrest me, arrest me. What the hell would you be arresting me for?" David was becoming incandescent now and found it difficult not to express his anger outwardly.

"Because you are refusing to accept this warning, Sir," the officer stated.

"But of course I am. Why would anyone accept something that they knew to be a lie? Anyway, I do not think these warnings have any legal power, do they, officer?" David stated with a strong degree of positivity. His anger had turned to confidence as he realized that he was being played by the officer. The officer had attempted to unnerve David from the moment that he entered the clinic in his forceful, aggressive manner.

PC Oliver had obviously assumed that if he could imply that this warning was an illustration of a serious misdemeanour, then perhaps he could cajole David into signing the form, which, if anything progressed, could be used to damn David in a court situation.

What the officer did not know is that David had received a similar warning following his divorce from Susan. The resultant depression had caused him to write a number of emails to Susan that had caused her such consternation, or so she had said, that she had been directed by a friend to go to the Police. The police had called David into the station and informed him of the complaint and stated that, although they understood the very unfortunate circumstances that had unfolded, he needed to refrain from any further contact with Susan of this nature. David explained, in detail, the turmoil that he had been through and accepted the line in the sand that this interaction had caused. He realized that the law and the system always fell on the side of the woman, and that it was therefore needless and unproductive to contest the situation.

Due to his inquisitive personality, David subsequently researched the legal nature of a Harassment Warning issued by the Police. It had been introduced as a policy a number of years previously, as a way of trying to calm down domestic disputes. In general, the issue of a harassment warning by one party to another resulted in an immediate reciprocal issuing of a counter-warning.

The concerning thing was that the police did not undertake any investigations, to attempt to validate the legitimacy of the original complaint made by the apparently aggrieved party. They chose to issue a warning notice that, irrespective of the fact as to whether there were any actual truths to the allegations, would cause reflection by all parties, and a curtailing of any harassment, if it did, in fact, exist in the first place.

The flaw in the police policy was that those who were aware of the perception of most of the public to the receipt of an official police warning, and the lack of police investigation as to the validity of the complaint, could use the warning to inappropriately denigrate someone's reputation. This was reinforced by the fact that the warning did not have a time factor to it. Once a warning had been issued, it could be used to effect potential court proceedings many years later.

"Respectfully, PC Oliver, and I say respectfully, despite the fact that you do not seem to have shown me an ounce of respect, from the moment you walked into my clinic. Respectfully, we both know that this warning has little effect, does it? You have not investigated these allegations at all. All you have done is receive them and assume that they are creditable and valid, based on the flawed premise that no one, who was not experiencing the harassment that they were purporting, would take the time to present to a police station and make such a complaint. But from your overall experience in police work, you know that people lie all the time. So, I know that you cannot arrest me for this in any way, shape, or form, PC Oliver, and you know it too. So, I strongly suggest that you retract your statement that unless I sign this form, you will arrest me, and then I can present to you evidence that proves, without any doubt, that the statement that caused you to issue this warning is nothing more than total bullshit".

David felt his composure return throughout his diatribe to the officer. It had been a very unfortunate experience that he had gone through that caused Susan to issue her warning, but if it had not happened, he would not have been at all knowledgeable of the effective meaninglessness of a Harassment Warning and, therefore, may well have inadvertently signed this form presented by PC Oliver.

PC Oliver had been totally surprised by David's robustness. On every occasion previously, when he had presented himself in an aggressive manner and tone, whilst issuing other Harassment Warnings, as soon as he had threatened an arrest, the recipient had complied and signed the form.

PC Oliver considered his attitude and response now. He felt that he could not totally alter his tone as it would become very apparent that David knew, that he knew that, what David had said, was the

93

absolute truth. But as he did not have any substantive information to prove Mrs. Rossington's claims, he felt that he was duty-bound to be in possession of all the evidence available to be able to prove or disprove the complaint.

Thus, softening his tone slightly, in an attempt to give David an opportunity to show him evidence that countered Rossington's statement, PC Oliver said, "Well, if you feel that you have anything that could illustrate to me, that what Mrs. Rossington is saying is not correct, then I'd be happy to look at it."

David directed the officer back to the reception, where he spent the next 20 minutes showing PC Oliver, chronologically, the texts and emails received from and sent to Jenny Dolton / Mrs. Rossington. The policeman read, in near silence, as he realized that, in no way at all, were the communications anything more than friendly and supportive. At no time had Jenny requested that David did not contact her either, and thus there was no actual, implied or explicit harassment.

"Well, from what you have shown me, we have clearly been misinformed," PC Oliver stated in a much more considered manner than he had entered the clinic half an hour before.

"Also, if you also review statements logged by PC Franklin and PC Kendal when they visited my clinic a few weeks ago, being in receipt of a direct communication from Mrs. Rossington, regarding her concerns that her husband intended to have me beaten up, then you will have a better idea of the psychological state of this lady, which ought to enlighten you as to what is going on here. Namely, that she has been put up to presenting herself to the Police Station by her husband, in an attempt to damn my name and probably professional reputation." David explained very lucidly.

"So, with all that information from both my texts and from what you will glean from your colleagues, what are you going to do with that notice now, then," David asked, as he did not wish such a false record to remain associated with him in any way.

"Well, we cannot remove the notice once raised." the policeman said somewhat apologetically.

"Why not? You have clear evidence that she has made a false statement. You will also have more substantive information from your colleagues, so you must surely be able to remove the warning! Otherwise, would you not be facilitating a perversion of justice? Someone has arbitrarily turned up at a police station and, for whatever reason, from what you have seen, at the very least, vexatiously made a false statement. Surely, at the bottom of this statement, she would have to have signed to say that this was a true statement of fact? But you now know that it is nothing but a pack of lies. So could I counter that with action against her, in regards to deliberately and knowingly making false statements?" David was starting to get agitated again.

"The best I can do is to go back to the station and put a notice on the file to the effect that I have seen clear evidence that there was no harassment." Oliver offered.

"Okay, well, respectfully, how do I know that that will occur?" David questioned.

"Sorry, Mr. Roseman, are you questioning what I said I would do? I have spent time with you here, going through the messages, which I did not have to do." PC Oliver retorted.

David became bemused. Here was a policeman, who had arrived in a very aggressive manner on the superficial say-so of a woman. Hearsay that he had not questioned, or investigated, but assumed to be truthful, which he had subsequently seen clear evidence that the woman was lying, and yet he wondered why someone might question the integrity and intended actions following.

"I'm sorry, officer, but following what I have experienced in recent weeks and this morning, it is not at all surprising that I am somewhat untrustworthy, is it?" David raised his eyebrows at the officer as he finished his comment.

PC Oliver acknowledged David's concerned comments, but could not offer any further reassurance and duly left, with David presuming that he would add the note to the file, as he had indicated that he would.

Over the weekend, David spent a considerable time thinking as to why someone would deliberately take the time to drive 15 miles to a police station and then make a statement, that they knew to be false. The conclusion had to be either that Jenny was a very devious and manipulative individual, who enjoyed creating drama, to facilitate excitement in her otherwise drab and mundane life. Or that she really was married to a very aggressive, vicious, vindictive man, who she was so frightened of that she had to invent a situation of harassment, to attempt to prove, how she had been treated, assuage her guilt, in regards to her true feelings, and therefore why she might have engaged in the communication with David, that she had.

A thought that persisted in David's head related to the circumstance in which a woman, who, having been with someone for over two years, and who would be very cognizant of his personality and character, and his traits and failures, particularly his extreme possessiveness, and his aggressive, controlling nature, would deliberately not put a security password on her phone, when especially she knew that due to previous experience, he had accessed her phone, without requesting to, and also knowing the presence of the messages on the phone.

The fact that the messages were only messages and communications between two friends was not the point. She would have known that the problem for her psychotic husband, was that they were messages with another man. Even if her memory of historic experiences had faded, the fact that her husband had gone berserk with their next-door neighbour, who had kindly travelled to Portugal for the wedding, taken the role of usher, and on his return, not unreasonably, or unnaturally posted photos of the wedding and his experience on Facebook, was seriously lambasted by Jenny's husband, and threatened in such an aggressive manner, as to ensure that he removed all the photos from the site, might have caused her to take some simple precautions.

The fact that she did not do what nearly everyone else would do, even those in a very trusting and stable relationship, and secure her phone, such that only she could access it, appeared somewhat suspicious.

Chapter 8 – The Accusation

A number of weeks passed, and life revolved around the normality of the day-to-day. The clinic was reasonably prosperous, but David continued to wish for more new patients, to grow the business back to somewhere close to where it had been before the divorce.

He realized that there was no need to achieve the exact patient numbers that he had seen personally, before the divorce, due to the fact that his overheads had reduced markedly. Two fundamentals had changed financially. First, due to now living above the clinic, he was only servicing one mortgage, and second that he no longer needed to furnish the salary of Lucy, his practice manager.

Lucy had worked at the clinic from almost its inception. David had come across her in the period of time that he had worked as a locum at Pudlingley. Lucy was the practice manager for a multi-disciplinary practice and was extremely proficient, efficient, and kind to both staff and patients.

When the original clinic was up on its feet and could service financially, a practice manager, David, considered only one person. Lucy had the correct temperament and personality, not only to suit the professional approach needed, but also the family-orientated atmosphere that both David and Susan had wished to portray. The fact that David still felt somewhat aggrieved by the way that he had been treated by the GP, Philip Pargetter, who owned the complementary clinic and had seen the opportunity of destabilizing that clinic, with the removal of Lucy, in her practice manager's role there, added to his drive to employ her.

However, Lucy left Silkmoor Chiropractic Clinic when patient numbers had reduced, mostly due to the onset of David's depression, during the period of the divorce. It was a very sad day when Lucy left the clinic. But conversely, the lack of the burden of her salary meant that the clinic needed to see fourteen fewer patients a week to return the same level of profit.

David was aware, that the lack of a practice manager and the human interaction that was provided when patients arrived, deprived the clinic of some of the atmosphere that had been the case when Susan was also there. But, had Lucy not left, the clinic would not have remained viable.

The post usually arrived at around 9.40. a.m. The post lady was a very affable woman and had, in the past, been a patient of the clinic. The heavy mailbags that the postal delivery people had to wear, caused persistent issues with low back pain. The evolution of a policy of the delivery person not having to carry all the post on their round, from the beginning of the round, but having postal drop-off points throughout the round, had reduced the incidents of injury. Consequently, it had been a number of years since this lady had felt the need for treatment.

David was not the most efficient at opening the post, and it was not unknown for letters to remain unopened for a few days. However, on this occasion, at approximately 9.40 am., the post lady entered the clinic reception with an A4 envelope that required a signature as confirmation of delivery. David duly signed the delivery notice, whilst observing that the letter was from his governing body, the Chiropractic Board of the United Kingdom.

His first thought, on receiving a letter from the CBUK that needed signing, was that he had been selected as one of the small percentage of chiropractors who were annually requested to provide additional proof of the Continued Professional Development (CPD).

Each year, like most other professionals, chiropractors had to undertake CPD to prove that they were keeping up to date with any relevant developments in the profession. There was a requirement to undertake individual personal development and also development with fellow professionals. The individual development could be reading professional magazines, or doing some personal research. The shared experience was generally covered by attendance at an annual conference. In fact, it was well understood that it was probably the existence of CPD that had enabled annual professional conferences to survive.

Across all professions, delegates attended annual conferences, where it was purported that they would learn something to improve their experience as a clinician. However, in nearly 20 years of practice, what David and his peers had actually shared, was the experience that most conferences just regurgitate information that was taught in their undergraduate years. But no one complains because simply attending, and being presented with your attendance certificate, satisfies the annual requirement for part of one's annual CPD liability.

David had been chosen approximately eight years ago to submit his detailed CPD and had presumed that due to the balance of probability, his turn was soon to come again. Since the divorce and the reduction in income of the clinic, it had been difficult to afford to attend conferences, and the shared chiropractic experience had been somewhat tenuous for some years. Thus, there was always a degree of trepidation when an official letter arrived from the CBUK.

David thanked the post lady for the delivery, and as he did not have a patient for 40 minutes, he opened the official letter.

As soon as he had read the short standard official letter of introduction, his heart sank, his mouth became instantly dry, and he could feel the palpations of his heart.

The document delivered by the post lady ran to numerous pages, of at least five documents, from first perusal.

The Chiropractic Board of the United Kingdom had received a letter of complaint from someone they would refer to in correspondence as "Patient A". Patient A, otherwise known as Jenny Dolton / Mrs. Rossington, had lodged a series of 13 complaints, all within the category of Unacceptable Professional Conduct.

The complaints ranged from an accusation that David had kissed her inappropriately in the treatment room, during treatment, to the fact that he had unexpectedly taken her to lunch whilst she was a patient at the clinic.

To compound the situation, she had also stated that due to the unwanted behaviour of David, she had had to report him to the Police, which resulted in a formal "Harassment Warning" from the Police.

The main document outlined the 13 accusations. Supplementary documents provided the "defendant" detailed information in regards to the procedure that would now be followed. The most concerning of these elements of procedure, related to the "Continued Fitness to Practice Hearing".

The penny now dropped as to why Jenny Rossington had gone to the Police to accuse him of harassment. It was so that she could add this to her complaint, and, as it involved an action by the Police, it would make the accusations appear much more damning.

The mantra of the CBUK was to "Protect the Public". This important element of running a governing body, and a profession, was well understood and accepted by all practicing chiropractors. The thing that always concerned chiropractors was the fact that their governing body did nothing to improve the reputation of chiropractic within the public domain. The body that was funded by extortionate subscription charges from the chiropractors, that had to call themselves Registrants and not Members, did very little, in the opinion of most registrants, to further the reputation of the profession that they served.

The lack of balanced opinion and respect that the CBUK has for its registrants is reflected by the Continued Fitness to Practice Hearing. The premise by which this hearing was set up was based on the perception that if they had received a serious complaint from one person, in regards to a chiropractor, then it might well be that this chiropractor had acted in a similar way, with other patients and therefore, just due to being in receipt of the complaint, for which there had been no investigation, and no substantiation, beyond the uncorroborated word of one person, they may feel it necessary to suspend the chiropractor, during the collation, and collection of evidence in relation to the complaint received, so as to protect the public from similar actions outlined by the sole complainant. The fact that the previous record, and years of unblemished practice, covering almost 70,000 treatments in a 16-year period, without a single hint of a complaint previously, was a matter of unquestionable record, did not have any bearing on the need to undertake a Fitness to Practice Hearing.

The fact that one person could write a letter of accusation of a sexual nature was all that was needed to trigger such a hearing.

David had been trained to notify his association in any circumstance where he received a letter of complaint from the CBUK.

David needed to ring the English Chiropractic Association (ECA) to notify them of his predicament.

Whilst he was dialing the number of the ECA, the one thing he wished was that Rose Coventry was still involved in the ECA. The ECA is the largest association for chiropractors in the United Kingdom. Rose Coventry was a woman who had the knowledge and the attention to detail, in conjunction with the motherly approach of wishing to care for every chiropractor who was a member of the organization, that she ran.

Rose was a woman who was straight talking but also extremely caring in the same breath. Sadly, since her retirement, the gravitas and the competence of the ECA had slid down the pan markedly.

"Good morning, the English Chiropractic Association. Sarah speaking, how may I help you?"

Good morning Sarah. It's David Roseman here. May I speak with someone who deals with professional conduct matters, please?" David asked in a very deliberate and considered manner.

"Yes, certainly, David. Is it an ongoing matter or a new situation?" Sarah asked politely.

"It's a new complaint". David replied.

"Okay, thank you, I'll put you through to Vivienne," Sarah said as the phone went to hold mode.

"Hello David, Vivienne speaking, how may I help".

David outlined the fact that he had received a notification of a complaint from the CBUK and of an impeding Fitness to Practice Hearing consequently.

Vivienne informed David that she would notify the insurers and that they would assess the case, in essence, to see whether it was something that was covered by the professional indemnity insurance, that every member, who was a member of the ECA had as a matter of right. If the truth is known, it was only the existence of the professional indemnity insurance, and the fact that the ECA ran two conferences a year to assist chiropractors in signing off on their shared attendance for their CPD, that was the reason any chiropractor was a member.

The phone call lasted no more than three minutes and resulted in David being told to expect a call from the insurers, informing him as to whether the insurance would cover this type of complaint or whether, despite many years of paying a considerable amount into the ECA, to cover professional indemnity, he would have to cover any legal costs himself.

The remainder of the morning of October 18th passed off unremarkably, although David found his focus of attention towards his patients, somewhat diminished by the constant revolving thought in his mind as to why someone, whom he had shown nothing but care and concern towards, would choose to attempt to ruin his professional career.

Three days later, on 21st October, the clinic phone rang. On answering, David heard a very well-educated, softly-spoken Scottish accent on the other end.

"Could I speak with Dr. David Roseman, please?"

"Speaking, how may I help?" David replied with a degree of nervous apprehension.

"My name is Josephine Barriston from Bellman's solicitors. I have been asked to contact you via your insurers, in regards to a complaint that you have received from the CBUK".

A telephone conversation ensued where Josephine Barriston outlined the information that was required and the broadest concept of how matters would proceed until the first, most important hurdle, the Fitness to Practice Hearing.

Josephine was a very dedicated solicitor who specialized in professional conduct law. She was in her mid to late twenties and was very particular about what was required.

David felt that she would be very competent in her undertakings, although somewhat pedantic, which may cause an element of frustration, as she may not be strong enough, or experienced enough to deal with his personality, or character. However, following their conversation, he felt relieved that there was someone who would be focusing on supporting him, in his attempts to clear his name, and as importantly, all and any legal costs would be covered by his professional indemnity insurance.

The drive to Bellman's offices in Manchester was uneventful. Due to always having Wednesdays off, arranging a conference with Josephine and her senior colleague on a Wednesday had no negative effect on the clinic.

Not surprisingly, Bellman's offices were located on the fourth floor of a relatively new office development, in the commercial quarter of Manchester. It never failed to disgust David how much solicitors charged and, consequently, how prestigious the offices in which they located themselves always were. David had had reason to engage solicitors, most recently, in regards to his divorce, and in addition to the pain of the divorce, the similarly severe pain related to the scale of fees that solicitors felt totally at ease charging.

The one satisfaction that David felt sitting in the plush leather upholstered chair in the large waiting area, serviced by a very high-tech reception desk, was that, on this occasion, whatever the cost of the fees generated by this law firm, and the barrister that may well need to be employed to carry the case, none of it would fall at his door. With that realization percolating through his veins, David felt himself sit back, stretch out his legs and enjoy the decadence of the solicitors' office space.

Josephine Barriston walked purposefully into reception and directly towards David. She was a slim, extremely well-dressed woman, who David had correctly envisaged was in her mid-twenties.

"Good morning David. Nice to meet you. Did you manage to find us, okay?" Josephine greeted David with a smile.

David had always wondered why everyone always asked if they had managed to find them okay when they first met. If they had not managed to find them okay, it would be quite probable that they

106

would not be sitting in the waiting area they were meant to be in, in good time for the meeting that had been arranged.

"Yes, fine, thank you," responded David.

Josephine marshaled David into a large conference room overlooking the arena outside. Sitting at the table and getting to his feet as they entered was Jason Brownley, a reasonably well-dressed, dark-haired man in his late thirties.

Jason smiled as he offered his hand to David and ushered him to sit at the end of the conference table.

David was not sure if everyone had the same ability as him to do the same, but he felt he could size up the character and personality of anyone within seconds of first meeting them. Josephine, he had concluded, would be a dedicated workhorse who would put every effort into securing the best possible outcome for her client. Jason, on the other hand, appeared to be someone who had been elevated to his position, more due to time spent, rather than ability and intellect. Jason gave the impression of someone who might be using law as a vehicle for a move into politics. His smile was somewhat superficial, and his handshake lacked any form of surety and gravitas.

However, it was clear that Jason was the senior member of the team with whom David was consulting this afternoon. It was explained that Josephine would be doing the legwork, with Jason in charge of the presentation to the CBUK panel at the Fitness to Practice Hearing. Instantly David felt somewhat cold at the prospect of relying on Jason to secure his future tenure in practice.

Although Jason had all the necessary papers in front of him, it was clear that he had not studied the case in any depth whatsoever.

"So, the purpose of this meeting, David is for you to tell us, in your own words, what happened during your various appointments with this patient," Josephine started.

"But isn't that what we spent two long conversations doing over the last two weeks?" David replied, somewhat frustrated that he was in a meeting in Manchester, to repeat what he had said over the telephone at least once already.

"Yes, that's true," Josephine responded. "But we need to go through things in detail so that we can understand exactly what you might be admitting and, of course, not admitting".

"Well beyond admitting to taking this lady as a patient, attempting to improve her acute pain, and once I had discharged her, realizing what she said her feelings were, I fell foul of attempting to show some concern for her as a friend, for someone, who I naively believed needed some help".

"So you refute, kissing her and buying her flowers, David, do you," Jason asked in a more than questioning manner.

"Yes, I most definitely do! I feel that I have been caught in an almost perfect storm. The aftermath of my divorce left me in a psychologically difficult place. A place where, had the money been no option, I would have probably removed myself from practice for a period, to recover. But finances meant that I had to keep practicing. The arrival of an attractive woman in the clinic, who, for some reason, chose to flatter me, turned my head somewhat, and I let the boost to my damaged emotions and ego, take precedence over my clinical and professional judgment. However, my only failure was not to discharge her a couple of treatments sooner, immediately, I realized that she had some interest in me. Then taking time to attempt to help her in what I thought was a very difficult dilemma, by listening to her and being a shoulder for her. That said, I do not think that showing some concern for her was wrong. The compromising situation was the time between discharging her and then meeting her socially for lunch. But as I have already said to Jo, this only occurred, due to the constrictions of circumstance, based on discharging her only eight days before she was due to go away to Portugal to get married. If she was in distress about her future, it seemed pointless to wait until after she got married to try and help her out of the problem of whether she could actually get married in the first place".

Both Josephine and Jason said nothing but smiled warmly, with a degree of sympathy for David's plight.

"But I understand that you continued the relationship after she returned from her wedding too". Jason stated pointedly.

"Wow, wow, wow, here. You guys are pedantic about the use of vocabulary, so please, let's be clear, at the most, it was a friendship. It was never a relationship. Of course, one has to define what is meant by both, but to my mind, a relationship between two adults imagines some physical interaction, if not sexual, and in no way was there anything physical, and definitely not sexual".

David stated before reflecting for a moment. "But the thing that concerns me is this Fitness to Practice Hearing. How on earth can the CBUK take the word of one patient, without any form of investigation, and potentially give it so much credence as to extrapolate that, if they have received such a complaint, that they need to protect the public from the possibility of a similar action happening again. There is no proof of what she said in the first place. It's all just hearsay and her word against mine. Surely, in the realms of

109

probability, if one considers the practice of someone, for in excess of 16 years, undertaking around 70,000 treatments, with approximately 50% of them involving women, and there being absolutely no issues whatsoever in this time, isn't it much more probable that this one woman, might have fabricated a story, for whatever reason, we do not know, but in the realms of probability isn't that the direction one might think the pendulum may have swung?"

"You make a very good point," Jason said in a slightly derisory tone.

"I make a very good point? Of course, I make a very good point because it's the truth. In my position, and particularly now as I practice by myself, I am potentially vulnerable to an accusation of professional misconduct, every time I take on a new female patient. I cannot have CCTV in the treatment room, as that could lead me to be accused of an act of voyeurism. I cannot afford to have someone chaperoning every female patient, just in case she is a nutcase. Females, although gowned, are in a state of semi-undress on most occasions when I treat them. It's my word against theirs. What am I supposed to do to protect myself? I can't. And then I have a governing body that only considers the words of one patient, with no thought or credibility towards the clinician, and consequently, they can allow such a situation to unfold without any opportunity to look at the history of a clinician. This is so wrong, so, so wrong!" David stated, almost spitting out the words as he said them.

David could feel a tear in his eyes, as his passion over the injustice of being seen as the villain, in a situation where all he attempted to do was to help people out of their pain, was being mischaracterized, leading him to be falsely accused.

Chapter 9 – Fitness to Practice Hearing

The Fitness to Practice Hearing had been arranged to be held at the International Dispute Resolution Centre, in Fleet Street, London, on Friday, 18th November 2016. The date of the hearing was less than a month from the receipt of notification of the CBUK complaint.

In the interim period, Josephine Barriston had directed David to ask as many patients as practicable, if they could produce letters of support in relation to their experience as patients at Silkmoor Chiropractic Clinic, and specifically as patients of David.

The concept of engaging with a patient, particularly a female patient, and having to explain that he had been accused of inappropriate behaviour, of a sexual nature, as a precursor to asking a patient if they would write a letter of support, went against certain principles that David held true. First, the idea that one had to openly notify patients of longstanding, with whom David had built up a considerable amount of trust, that he had been accused of something that had been classified as being of a sexual nature, did not seem correct. But further, once that statement was out in the open, to then solicit a request from that patient to write a letter of support, seemed to potentially put the patient under a degree of pressure that they should not be put under.

David had had lengthy conversations with Josephine Barriston on this matter, the result being that he felt that she did not quite grasp the sensitivity of the relationship that David had with his patients. All patients have to have a fair degree of trust in a chiropractor, as at each appointment, the chiropractor has to encroach within the patient's personal space. The space that the patient reserves only for close relatives and family, and often not a space within which they would readily allow a longstanding friend to enter, let alone a total stranger. The fact that many female patients had been comfortable allowing David to work on them, within this personal space, and in some cases, for many years, might be undermined by them considering any accusation of a complaint, in relation to anything of a sexual nature.

As it turned out, David's reticence and anxiety, in regards to his patients' writing letters of support were without foundation. In the three weeks between the notification of the hearing and the hearing itself, David asked 14 female patients if they would mind providing a letter of support, and within a few days, he received 14 very flattering letters of support. He felt somewhat emboldened by the response.

In order to get to Fleet Street for a 9.00 a.m. start, it was necessary to catch the 5.45 a.m. train from Leeds to London Kings Cross. Connecting trains from Silkmoor to Leeds did not start running until 6.02 a.m., and therefore it was necessary to drive to Leeds and leave the car in the station car park, which, surprisingly, was not the exorbitant cost for the day that David had expected.

The night before, he had considered, at length, what he should wear. Should he wear a suit, or a jacket and tie and trousers? If he wore a suit, the only one that he had was a Saville Row suit that he had bought as a treat to himself when he was recovering from his depression. During the two and a half years of his depression, David had often found himself in one of the local pubs in Silkmoor, looking for some kind of solace. In one particular pub, he had befriended a guy who co-owned a Saville Row shop in Harrogate. Gordon had offered to sell David an off-the-peg suit at a knockdown price. A price even reduced from the sale price. It was a three-piece suit that was beautifully styled, and when his daughter Eleanor first saw him in it, she asked if he was going to a wedding.

Prior to buying it, David had always wondered why someone would spend what could be considerable money on a suit. However, once it was on, it was clear. The feeling of increased self-esteem was instant, and the sense of confidence was clear to any observer. The fact that many British men looked with such distain, when they saw David wearing it, only confirmed the appalling disregard with which most British men chose to dress.

David's dilemma was whether the suit would appear too much of a statement to the panel and whether the wearing of it would be misconstrued as being arrogant or aloof. Or would appear assured and professional. In the end, he chose the compromise of wearing it to elevate his self-esteem, but only as a two-piece, not as a three-piece.

When David arrived and passed through the ticket barrier at Leeds station, the London Kings Cross train was sitting on the platform. It was the second train of the day to London, and it started at Leeds. David had chosen not to book a seat and therefore had to take his chances in finding a seat that did not have a paper reserved ticket stuck in the top of it. Of course, without a detailed study of the tickets, it was not possible to know from whence the seat was booked. Often as it turned out, due to the train getting busier and busier with passengers, the closer the journey came to London, a large proportion of the seats were not actually booked until halfway to London, from places like Peterborough or Grantham. Thus, passengers who were only going from Leeds to Newark or Retford may needlessly find themselves without a seat on the presumption that all of them were booked for the whole journey.

Luckily, as soon as he got on the train, he came across an unreserved seat around a table of four. He chose the forward-facing aisle seat. A few minutes later, the train duly left Leeds on time. The majority of the carriage was empty. At the first stop, Wakefield, some fifteen minutes from Leeds, a man got on and chose to sit in the aisle seat opposite David. Although David was sitting in the opposing aisle seat, and the window seat was available, this gentleman chose to sit directly opposite. David lifted his head from the script he was learning for the play he was due to be performing in later in the summer of 2017, to acknowledge his new companion. The man deliberately chose not to offer any form of courteous acknowledgement. David smiled at the lack of common decency of the man and returned to his script. The man, who had removed his laptop from his bag before he sat down, opened up the lid as soon as he felt settled. David smiled once again as he noticed, over the next ten minutes, how the man slowly moved his laptop increment by increment to take over more of the space on the table between the two of them. What was it about people, who clearly one presumed held down very well-paid jobs, to be commuting, on a daily basis from Leeds to London, who did not have the common decency to engage in the most basic of courtesies? At the next station, more commuters got on. This time, another two individuals took the remaining seats around the table, both independent of each other, and neither with any intention of engaging in even menial conversation with anyone. Why was it people would prefer to stand directly at the side of a seated person's elbow, at such close proximity, as to ensure that the seated person was aware of them, and when the seated person lifted their head, the person stood up, would lift their head sharply in the direction of the vacant window seat, intimating that they wished to sit on that empty seat? Why didn't people converse? Was it exposing a sense of insecurity to talk

114

to a stranger?, or did it indicate subservience to say, "Excuse me, but may I sit in there?"

The lack of civility and common courtesy was something that would easily annoy David, and he would often play a game to expose the impoliteness of others.

"It always fascinates me how everyone lives inside a virtual bubble when commuting, pretending that no-one other than themselves is sharing the same environment," he said, whilst turning his head and directing his comment towards the lady sitting beside him in the window seat, who was holding up a foolscap newspaper, covering her face both front and side.

There was a pause as the lady, who was clearly aware that David had directed the comment towards her, assessed her situation. She was hemmed in by this man, with whom she clearly was not programmed to enter into conversation, whom she hoped, that if she pretended to give the impression that she had not heard his comment, over the silence of the carriage, would leave her alone. The fact that the lady chose not to respond, beyond pulling the edge of her paper closest to David, nearer to her face, confirmed David's beliefs.

The remainder of the journey to London was uneventful. The train pulled into platform eight at Kings Cross, and the passengers charged out of the exit in their rush to get to work.

In order to prepare himself and clarify matters in his mind, David had decided to walk a couple of miles to Fleet Street. Having lived in London for seven years, when he worked there as an architect, David knew London very well. The walk from Kings Cross station was relatively direct, going straight down Graves End Road to

Holborn and then meandering its way through some back streets until arriving at Fleet Street.

The weather on arrival in London was mild, and the bright sunshine took the edge off what might have been a chilly morning, bearing in mind that it was mid-November.

David's emotions oscillated during the walk. In his heart, he felt relaxed, as he knew the truth and the fact that the whole predicament that he was being put through was unjust, and if there was karma, he would be walking back along Graves End Road, in a few hour's time, vindicated by the presence of the truth. However, conversely, the reason that he was here was that the truth of the events had not been investigated, and the hearing at which he was appearing today had been set up on the premise of "what if".

What if the complaint was found to be true? Then perhaps a similar situation might occur in the future, and quite possibly during the period in which this complaint was being investigated.

One of the greatest frustrations was that no one seemed to consider the probability. What was the probability of someone who had practiced for 16 years, administrating around 70,000 treatments, , with in excess of 3,000 women new patients, having a history of inappropriate sexual behaviour? Further, in the knowledge of the complaint being investigated, what was the likelihood of that person acting in a similar manner to any patient during the period of the investigation?

Speaking with Josephine Barriston about the time frame of the events of the day, she had stated that it should all be over by lunchtime.

The International Resolution and Dispute Centre was a nondescript building at the lower end of Fleet Street. As David walked through the revolving entrance door, he noticed a signboard that he presumed would indicate on which floor his hearing was located.

"Good morning Sir. Can I help you" the receptionist asked before he had time to study the board.

"Good morning. I'm looking for the location of a CBUK hearing," David politely asked.

The receptionist studied her list. "It's on the fourth floor, Sir. Can I take your name for your identity, please?" she smiled at David.

"It's Doctor David Roseman."

"Ah, yes. Can I ask you to put on this identity card, please, Sir". The receptionist handed David a pre-prepared name card. David studied it "**Mr. David Roseman – Defendant**".

Reading the card, a wry smile crossed his face. David was not unique in his disbelief of the CBUK's attitude to its registrants. Although his title as a chiropractor and whose qualifications were one of only a few professions whose titles were protected by statute, the CBUK would always chose to address their registrants as "Mr" or "Miss or "Ms" and not "Dr". However, if the chiropractor stated that they wished to be addressed as "Dr" in accordance with the title they had been awarded, by successfully attaining the qualification of a chiropractor, at a college run under the jurisdiction of the CBUK, then the CBUK would capitulate and address the chiropractor by the title he or she had attained at the completion of their training. What was that all about? Why did the CBUK not act in a respectful way to the people who paid their salary, and without whom, there would be no need for the body in the first place?

David never used his title in any interaction with his patients, but when it related to a professional matter, he felt that he had earned the right to be addressed as a doctor. He was being demeaned enough to have to present himself to this forum today, through no fault of his own. The very least that he should expect was for his accusers to address him by the title that he had spent five years attaining.

David was directed to the lift. When he arrived on the fourth floor, it became evident that the floor was divided into two halves around the lift lobby. At each level, there was the capacity to have two separate events, occurring simultaneously.

Arriving early, David was able to walk around the floor to familiarize himself with the layout. There were two very small meeting rooms, two larger rooms, and one "courtroom". The small meeting rooms were nondescript and clearly ante chambers for consultation, between no more than three or four people. The larger rooms contained ash-veneered conference tables that would allow approximately twelve people to sit around them. The courtroom, on the other hand, was somewhat more oppressive in its layout. It was approximately five metres square, and the focal point was a small raised dais, on which was a table, behind which were four large high-backed leather chairs. On the table and directly in front of each chair were individual microphones. Opposite this dais were two distinct areas, each with two small square tables, put together to make one rectangular table, each with two chairs behind them. Behind these was another row replicating the front row. These tables also had microphones placed upon them.

David's first impression was that the layout, and in particular the large high-backed chairs, on which the adjudicating panel would sit, were somewhat over the top and were only there to attempt to unnerve anyone who entered the room, particularly as an inexperienced witness, or a first-time defendant.

Arriving early, David was able to walk freely around the various rooms and facilities. In the main "courtroom," he came across a lady who was placing various papers, pens, and pencils on the desks.

"Good morning", David politely greeted the woman.

"Good morning, lovely day" the lady replied with a smile.

Well, it might have been weather-wise, David thought. But otherwise, the correctness of that statement had to be held over until the end of the hearing, from his perspective.

"Are you from the CBUK?" David asked quizzically.

"Yes" the lady replied.

"Could you tell me how long these sorts of hearings last, please?" In part, David was only asking to make conversation, as he had been told by Josephine Barriston that it should be over by lunchtime.

"They usually go on most of the day" the woman replied.

"Oh, that's a shame. I was told that it would be finished by lunchtime, hence the reason I have bought a return ticket for a train at 3.30 p.m."

"Oh, I doubt that it will be over by then, I am afraid," the woman remarked as she left the courtroom.

That was the first disappointment of the day. David hoped that it would also be the last.

Twenty minutes later, Josephine Barriston and Jason Brownley arrived. The three of them then encamped themselves in one of the small conference rooms. After a brief from Brownley about what would be happening during the hearing, they waited to be called.

During the briefing, David was somewhat concerned at the scruffily quickly handwritten notes he noticed in front of Brownley. Notes he presumed had only been made during the train journey from Manchester to London this morning.

At 9.45 a.m., the usher called them to attend the courtroom. In addition to David and Brownley, who sat on the front row, with Josephine sitting directly behind, what David presumed to be the CBUK barrister sat on an adjacent desk. A stenographer sat close to the dais, and the usher hovered expectantly.

A few minutes later, a door at the rear of the room opened, and four people walked solemnly into the room. As they entered, Brownley leant over towards David and directed him to stand. The panel then sat on the high-backed leather chairs. In the centre was a stiff-faced-looking woman in her late fifties. She was flanked on either side by two other women. At the right end of the panel was a gentleman, who looked learned, and in his late sixties.

The panel nodded towards the assembled company, who dutifully nodded back. The chairwoman then took her seat, end everyone duly sat down.

The chair introduced herself and then asked the remaining members of the panel to introduce themselves respectively. The panel consisted of a lay member, a chiropractor, and the chair, who was a bureaucrat from the Dental Association. The gentleman on the panel was the legal adviser. Jason Brownley had expressed pleasure at seeing Norman Seabrook on the panel, sitting as the legal adviser. He had presented to him before and had found him a reasonable and considerate man, who had a subtle way of directing the panel towards his opinion, without outwardly telling them exactly what to do.

"Now that we have introduced ourselves, I would be appreciative to receive the opening remarks from the prosecuting side, followed by the Defense" the chair stated through the microphone on her desk.

This directed an Asian gentleman in his late twenties to rise. "Good morning, Madam chair, members of the panel. My name is Ingmar Hussain. I am representing the Chiropractic Board of the United Kingdom and will put the case why it is the opinion of the CBUK not to allow Mr. Roseman to practice whilst this investigation is ongoing".

David could feel his heckles rise. Once again, the CBUK had chosen to show blatant disrespect by addressing him as "Mr" as opposed to "Dr" in a formal situation. He was sure that the General Medical Council would not be so deliberately disrespectful when they were looking to take action against one of their members.

Hussain sat down with a cursory dismissive glance towards Jason and David, who were sitting within a couple of feet of him.

Once standing, Jason Bromley started his opening statement. "Madam chair and members of the panel, in our submissions to the panel, we will show that in his 16 years in practice, Dr David Roseman has had an exemplary career, been one of the very few chiropractors to have been commissioned by the NHS and has a 98%

patient satisfaction rating from an independent survey of his treatment outcomes. So, we will show that due to his exemplary career…

"Excuse me, Madam Chair, I am sorry to interject, but I cannot allow my colleague to misrepresent to the panel, by claiming that Mr. Roseman has had an exemplary career to date. I have evidence that Mr. Roseman does not have an exemplary record at all".

David looked with immense distain at Jason as he leant towards him, whispering. "What the bloody hell is this chap talking about. You need to challenge the information that he has and set the record straight. Otherwise, he might undermine our argument totally".

Jason switched his microphone on. "Excuse me, Madam Chair. This statement has taken us all by surprise. We do not have any idea as to what Mr. Hussain is eluding. May I request a short recess to speak with Mr. Hussain, to attempt to ascertain to what he is referring?"

Mr. Hussain seemed very pleased to interject. "Madam Chair, I understand that Mr. Roseman was the subject of a complaint to the CBUK back in 2008 which is on record, and thus I cannot accept the statement that his record is exemplary."

"Do you have a clue as to what he could be referring David?" Jason whispered.

"The only thing that happened around that time is that, subsequent to action taken by the English Chiropractic Association against a self-serving journalist, who defamed the ECA in an article in the Guardian, this journalist raised complaints against every chiropractor who had a website at the time. The resultant was that the CBUK was presented with complaints against over 70% of all the chiropractors in the country. This chap questioned certain statements on our websites. However, what the CBUK did not ascertain before they initiated the investigations against us all, was that all we had done was to publish, verbatim, information that had been presented to us by our governing body, which, as you will know, is the CBUK. So effectively, the CBUK were giving credibility to a guy who was looking to complain against over 700 chiropractors, for using information, on each of our websites that was already in the public domain, via the fact that the CBUK had already published it, in their own literature. Due to the procrastination of the CBUK, it took them over a year to realize that they could not really adjudicate against chiropractors using information that they, the CBUK, had published, as to do so would undermine their own credibility. So, what this dickhead has done, in his very short time of preparation, is to see the headline complaint statistic, but not followed up on finding anything in detail about the complaint. So, we need to inform him in such a manner that he apologises for his misrepresentation." David, although still whispering, was clearly becoming exasperated that some misinformed idiot was attempting to defame him, based on not having a handle on the facts.

"Madam Chair, I wondered if I might ask for a few minutes' recess so that I might consult with Mr. Hussain to clarify matters in regards to Dr. Roseman's exemplary career?" Jason asked.

"Certainly, Mr. Brownley, if you feel that the opposing counsel is misinformed, I will give you a short recess. Mr. Hussain, would you be accepting of a short consult with Mr. Brownley, please?'

"Certainly, Madam Chair," Hussain responded.

At that point, Hussain, Brownley, and David left the courtroom.

Politely but particularly, Jason Bromley opened the dialogue. "Mr. Hussain, if you would look at the complaint to which you refer, you will realize that Dr. Roseman was one of 700 chiropractors complained about and that, when the CBUK investigated the nature of the complaint, they concluded that the complaint was unreasonable, unjustified and somewhat vexatious. Dr. Roseman was exonerated, as were all but 15 of the other 700 chiropractors who received a complaint. So therefore, as I stated in my opening address, Dr. Roseman does have an exemplary record, in his 16 years of practice".

Hussain bowed his head as he considered his response.

"Ok, I accept your directions," he responded somewhat meekly.

"Therefore, you need to inform the chair that you are withdrawing your dissension of my statement regarding Dr. Roseman's character," Jason smiled, knowing that he had put his adversary in his place, right at the start of the proceedings, a good place to be, as he politely directed Hussain.

The three returned to the courtroom.

"Madam Chair, having been provided with information that was not in my possession previously, I am happy to withdraw my statement, in regards to questioning Mr. Roseman's exemplary career to date and am happy to accept the opening remarks of Mr. Brownley." Hussain said, clearly realizing that his credibility had been questioned from the moment he first opened his mouth, attempting to appear sharp and combative and to undermine the Defense. But all he had done was to illustrate that he was ill-prepared.

Part of David's defense was the numerous letters of support from his current patients. Many of whom had been patients of his for over ten years. However, the most important letter of support came from Benjamin Hidelman. Benjamin was a retired Acting Chief Constable of the Police. Ben had been one of David's patients intermittently for a number of years. David had consulted Ben in relation to the Harassment Warning.

Not unsurprisingly, the presence of a Warning from the Police that had been issued to David from the complainant, had caused a fair degree of interest from the panel. Naturally, the layman's belief would have been that if the Police had taken it upon themselves to issue a formal warning, they would have investigated a complaint to such a level as to have found sufficient grounds to present to someone's property with an official warning.

Ben Hidelman produced documentation that dispelled the natural perception of the layperson. All that is required for the Police to issue a Formal Harassment Warning is for one party to present to the Police and state that they have been harassed.

Of course, what David was extremely clear about, was that the issuing of such a warning, due to the nature of Police involvement, could and would, if not clearly understood by those not within the Police, be incorrectly perceived as a "no smoke without fire" situation. There would be an implied slant on his character, even though there was no evidence to substantiate such a perception.

David had contacted Ben the day before the hearing to ask if he could provide anything substantive to clarify matters. At the time, Ben was on his way to The Hague, due to his work with counter-terrorism, to discuss matters with politicians and senior European policemen. Luckily for David, he managed to catch Ben in transit at Heathrow. Ben, in a couple of hours that he was waiting for his flight, was able to collate Police and newspaper documentation, clarifying the actual status of an Harassment Warning, and email it to Jason Brownley on the afternoon prior to the hearing.

During the briefing, prior to the hearing, Jason had referenced the document received from Ben, as the most important submission to the hearing. David considered the luck and co-incidence of circumstances that, on this occasion, had gone in his favour. The truth of the matter is that the facts of the status of the Warning were well known within the circles in which it was issued; however, if it had not been for Ben having a couple of hours to collate enough documentation, to inform and redirect the perception of the layperson, who knows what impression the panel might have had of David.

The resultant was that the presentation of the information allowed the panel to consider the personality of someone who would deliberately fabricate a complaint, so as to intentionally undermine the reputation of a professional. If this had happened, what was feasibly possible, in regards to the detail of the complaint?

From the moment the Chair had sat down, David was conscious that she was constantly assessing him. It was clear that the presentations by the barristers were not the only material by which she would be assessing the fitness of David to continue to practice, whilst the complaint was being investigated.

It was the first time in his life that David could remember being consciously under scrutiny by another individual. Being aware of the scrutiny caused him to attempt to ensure that he did not outwardly inform the Chair that he knew that she was studying him. However, he was conscious that such knowledge might set up a demeanour of being self-conscious about attempting not to be self-conscious. He considered his posture, both generally, in the way he sat on his chair, and all the more detailed elements of his posture, in terms of the location of his hands etc. He attempted to remember some psychological studies he had read in regards to putting one's hand on one's chin or through one's hair. The variety of possible contraindications he could be emitting caused him to smile to himself. He realized how difficult it was to be oneself and act naturally, when one was being stared at.

A few minutes after these various thoughts travelled through his mind, and at an appropriate juncture in proceedings, Josephine leant forward from the desk behind and remarked. "Just to let you be aware that the chair is studying you like a hawk David, so make sure you act naturally".

David smiled and, in his own head, thanked Josephine. He had thought he had got his relaxed mode under control, to such an extent as not to appear outwardly self-conscious. But Josephine's intervention, however well-meaning, only resulted in raising the level of his self-consciousness once again.

Was he perspiring? Did he look smug or conceited? At every moment, the concept that, due to the thought passing through his mind, this might cause him outwardly to reflect that thought started to mildly torture him. The worse thing that he could think was that he might look guilty, by the mere fact that he was attempting to look natural and innocent.

The hearing went through the various legal protocols for the rest of the morning. Just before 12.00 pm., the chair announced that, as it was almost time for lunch, she suggested that they adjourned for lunch and that the panel would then reconvene to discuss the various presentations at 2.00 pm. And hopefully have a resolution by 3.30 p.m.

The timeframe made David smile and only reflected the lack of consideration that the CBUK had for one of their registrants. Why, when they had only been sitting for two hours, did they then need a two-hour lunch break before sitting down to consider the submissions they had heard? It was clearly going to be a long three and a half hours.

The hearing adjourned, and David and his legal team decanted into their small office, whilst the panel went to reside in a much larger conference room.

"So, what happens now, and why do they need a two-hour lunch?" David directed his question to Jason Brownley.

"Well, they will do very little, if not nothing, until 2.00 p.m. The reason that they will take a two-hour lunch is that, if they started deliberating now, they may conclude their discussions before 1.00 p.m. If that were to happen, they may well feel it would be inappropriate to then take lunch before coming back for a 10-minute conclusion. But if they take a long lunch, they are assured of the hearing going on into the afternoon, and they are paid per half day."

"Sorry, Jason, so are you telling me that a group of people who have been chosen to adjudicate on my fitness to practice, based on their integrity and comprehension of appropriate professional principles, are the same people who have chosen to massage the day so that they can be assured of getting a day's pay as opposed to half a day's pay?"

"Yes." Jason responded, shyly shrugging his shoulders, in a manner as if to say, yes, I'm afraid that is how the legal system works.

"For fucks sake. I am here fighting for my career, my reputation, and the financial well-being of my children, due to the lies and deception of an insipid little shit and nutter of a woman and her aggressive, psychopathic husband, and the most critical consideration of those charged with that responsibility, is to think more about whether they get paid for the part, or all of a day. Where is the integrity in that? Fuck me!" They remove themselves from being creditable to be in a position to make such a decision by that action alone." David fumed.

"I'm sorry, David. Everyone only looks after themselves in this game." Jason offered.

"Clearly, Jason. Although I respect your candour, when you're sat in my current position, where you have no choice but to rely on others to ensure the continuance of your career and life, such openness and honesty is not at all comforting, I am afraid."

Once David had computed the hypocrisy of the whole system, he felt that the depth of the resultant silence that pervaded a small room was too much to sustain.

"I'm going off for a walk," he announced to his legal team.

David left the cramped room and walked towards the lift lobby, still cogitating the fact that his anxiety of having to wait for an outcome was being extended, for the sole reason that those on the panel could each pick up an additional £100 for still being there beyond 2.00 p.m.

Distracted by the intensity of his thinking, he quickly arrived at the lift lobby and stood waiting for the lift to arrive for a short while, before realizing that the person also standing waiting was the chair of the panel. He considered the gentlemanly option of exiting the building via the adjoining staircase, but decided that if he was being kept ill at ease unnecessarily for the sake of £100, then he would reciprocate by sharing the journey of the lift from the fourth to ground floor, with a chair who was clearly more than a little self-conscious about the situation.

The silence, for the 45 seconds that the lift took to arrive in reception, was palpable and comforted David immensely. If he had not known before, he realized, in that short period, that when someone is taken out of the context of an environment, where they have been given a hierarchy, and elevated status, by means of the size of the seat they are sat on, and the procedural ceremony of standing for their entrance, they are actually, no different to anyone else in reality.

In those 45 seconds, David recollected the intensity with which the Chair had attempted to ascertain who he was and what his true character and personality was, as she had stared at him persistently from her elevated podium. The lift duly arrived in reception.

As the doors opened, David deliberately stood to the side and, with confidence, stretched his arm out towards the door, clearly directing the Chair to exit before him. He smiled inside, as he knew that, as the Chair made a weak gesture of gratitude towards his chivalry, as she exited the lift, she had been provided a clear indication as to who this man was.

130

Being located in the lower end of Fleet Street, the International Conflict Resolution building was only a 5-minute walk from Aldgate and St Paul's Cathedral.

Like many people who either lived, or had lived in London, many of the iconic buildings that they had all promised themselves that they would visit whilst they lived there, or would be visited at some time, remained unexplored. Although David had lived in London for a total of 9 years, he had never ever visited St. Pauls. Ironically, today as effectively a "tourist" to the city, he chose to take a look.

In his years as an architect, he remembered the persistent arguments about the office and retail development in the area juxtaposed to St. Paul's. One of the reasons that David had decided to change careers from an architect to a chiropractor was based on the inane stupidity of the system, to embrace the development of architecture and allow the modern era to build to suit its time.

In centuries past, when a building of quality had been damaged by fire, those looking to rebuild it did not attempt to reproduce the technology of the original. They chose to respect the period in which they were rebuilding and act accordingly. However, now with the crazed sycophantic interest in conservation, it was almost a crime to build something of today, for today. David had always thought that if medicine had been shackled by the same reticence to move forward and embrace the modern era, that had constrained architecture, we would still be advocating bloodletting with leeches as the avante garde protocol in medical treatment.

Arriving at St. Paul's, he stood in the queue waiting to pay at the kiosk.

"Entry for one, please," he politely asked the lady in the kiosk.

"£32, please," she responded.

Aghast at the scale of the charge, David politely and silently smiled at the lady and turned tail, and walked out. He could not even get solace from a cathedral for an hour, without being ripped off. He smiled at the persistence of the injustice he was experiencing and walked away.

As directed, David returned to the International Resolution Dispute Centre at 2.30 p.m., Jason and Josephine were still chatting as he opened the door, only to stop the instant that they heard the door handle turn.

Somewhat embarrassed to have been caught out, Jason said, "They have said that they expect to return at about 3.00 pm."

"Oh, ok, thank you," David replied.

3.00 p.m. duly came and passed without any notification. Similarly, 3.30 p.m and 4.00 p.m.

"So, what do we take from the fact that they are taking longer to deliberate than the duration of the hearing?" David asked somewhat sarcastically. "There isn't a further financial incentive to sit beyond 4.00 p.m. by any chance, is there?"

Jason and Josephine both smiled embarrassingly. "I'll see if I can go and see how much longer they are going to be," Jason said as he got up from the table.

Two minutes later, Jason returned. "They have completed their deliberations, but they are having to wait for their conclusions to be typed up, distributed, and checked before they can reconvene".

"Why can't they do the admin after they have given the decision? They could email the document".

"I know, it's immensely frustrating," Josephine concurred.

Shortly after, there was a knock on the door, and the usher poked her head around the door and stated that they were ready to reconvene.

David, Jason, and Josephine positioned themselves in the same seats as previously in the courtroom. Once again, they stood as the panel entered from the opposite end of the room.

The Chair looked along the table to ensure that everyone was seated before leaning forward and turning on her microphone.

"Further to the presentations from both parties, we have deliberated, and it is our opinion, that due to the lengthy unblemished history that Dr. Roseman has had to this point, there are no circumstances that direct us to the belief, that allowing Dr. Roseman to continue to practice for the duration of the investigation into the complaint against would, in any way put the public at risk. Therefore, it is the direction of this panel that Dr. Roseman's fitness to practice is unquestioned and that we will not be imposing any sanctions whatsoever upon him, for the duration of the investigation. This hearing is now adjourned".

Everyone stood up as the panel vacated the courtroom. Jason turned and shook David's hand as Josephine leant forward and smiled.

Once back in their consultation room, Jason said, "Well, in my experience, you do not get those decisions very often."

"Why?," David asked inquisitively. "It really seems a bizarre setup to me in the first place. To take an accusation that is nothing more than one person's unproven statement and, without any investigation, give the accusation such credence as to consider suspending someone. To do so compounds the situation, and if the accusation is found to be unproven, but the chiropractor has been suspended, subject to the investigation and hearing, that the resultant be that he might lose his practice and career, when found, in the fullness of time to be innocent, is totally bizarre".

"The reason I say that we do not get those types of decisions very often is that the CBUK, in particular, have a very low bar that they need to satisfy, before they decide that suspension is the correct course of action. But that is academic in your case now".

David said his goodbyes to Jason and Josephine and walked the two miles back to Kings Cross station. The fact that he could not use the return portion of his ticket to Leeds, as the hearing had gone on beyond the time he had been informed, requiring him to purchase a single ticket to Leeds, seemed somewhat immaterial. However, come the end of the journey, having paid £120 for the single, that did not get checked, by anyone, at any time during the two-and-a-quarter hour journey to Leeds, did leave him somewhat frustrated.

As he prepared for his first patient at 7.00 a.m. the Monday morning following the hearing that could have suspended him indefinitely, the events of the previous Friday felt somewhat surreal.

"Good morning Martin. How are you? How was your weekend?" David nonchalantly asked his first patient of the morning, who had attended his weekly appointment for the last seven years.

Chapter 10 – Moving Forward

Once time had been allowed to settle, following the fitness to practice hearing, Josephine contacted David to inform him what would be happening during the period of investigation.

It appeared that the plaintiff would expand the extent of her complaint in writing. This would be submitted to the CBUK, who would forward the document to David for his responses. The plaintiff would then receive a copy of David's response to the details of her complaint and, if necessary, would have an opportunity to alter, amend or adapt her statements once more. If there were alterations, these would be sent to David for a further and final response. Josephine was specific in her directions that the accused had the last word of response.

In the first twelve weeks of 2017, David received a total of four statements from the CBUK. In each of the statements, he refuted statements made by Rossington. Due to the wayward nature of her statements, in which parts of each statement contradicted the content within previous statements, David took great satisfaction in outlining the contradictory nature of the content of the four statements that had been drafted by Rossington, each of which had been signed by her, as being a true and honest statement of the events that had occurred.

"Excuse me, Josephine. There are a number of things here that I do not understand and do not accept. First, I was told that Rossington only got two bites at the cherry, but in fact, she has had four. Secondly, there are comments made in one statement that are then totally contradicted in the following statements, and this is repeated from statement to statement ,across the four statements. So how come the CBUK does not see that this woman is lying through her teeth and dismiss the case?" David asked.

"If I am honest, David, I do not know. You're right. The complainant is only really allowed two bites of the cherry, as you say. However, it would appear that the CBUK are prepared to give her more. This will work in our favour, as it allows us to illustrate the persistent inaccuracies from her, and will help us to undermine her on the witness stand."

"But if there is a stipulated protocol and procedure, don't the CBUK have to abide by it?" David asked defiantly.

"Well, of course, yes, strictly, yes they do. But if we mention this to them, they might look unfavourably on us." Josephine replied.

"Why? If there is a procedure that, for whatever reason, has been established, that one party chooses not to adhere to, surely it is the obligation of the other party to direct that the defined procedure is respected. Otherwise, what is the point of the whole exercise?" David retorted.

"Oh, I very well understand where you are coming from, David, but please trust me, the fact that she is making more and more statements, that contradict earlier statements works in our favour, and not hers. So, it is best that we do not remind the CBUK of what they should do, as in negating the correct procedure, they are assisting our case." Josephine stated whilst smiling.

******

During his divorce, David had taken solace from spending many an evening in one of the local pubs. He had befriended a regular in one pub who was a very well-presented man, who co-owned a Saville Row outfitters in Harrogate. Gordon was an unmarried man in his early fifties, without any dependents known to him, who enjoyed a few pints of Guinness. He was someone who had a strong opinion on most issues of discussion.

Not surprisingly, the ups and downs of going through a divorce and the various scenarios relating to his children, his daughter in particular, were regular topics of conversation during the period that David was coming to terms with the emotional decimation that divorce creates.

Not long after the fitness to practice hearing had happened, David was in the Bulls Head pub chatting with Gordon. Gordon could always be found at a particular point at the end of the Bar. The conversation of the evening fluctuated from how their respective business had been in the week, to the daftness of the week's politics, to the detailed specification of the £6,000 mountain bike that Gordon was looking to buy in the near future.

Gordon always stood at the end of the bar, looking along the length of the bar. Consequently, anyone chatting to Gordon stood with his back to the length of the bar.

On this particular Friday evening, at a juncture in the evening when the conversation went a little quiet, David turned to gaze along the bar. Whilst perusing the pub, he quickly noticed a couple at the opposite end of the bar. He instantly recognized the outline of the woman who had her back towards him. He also became uncomfortably aware of the very unpleasant stare of the man accompanying the woman, who, due to her diminutive stature, allowed him to be able to look over her head.

Jenny Rossington was stood in a slightly provocative manner in a very tightly fitting pair of white jeans. Strangely though, it was clear that the nature of her pose was such that its provocative nature was not intended for her husband, but for anyone looking at her from behind. She stood with her left leg slightly in front of her right and slightly turned out. Her lumbar spine was extended somewhat, so as to accentuate the curvature of her bottom. Such a pose could only be taken in, and its nature understood, when viewed in a manner that would allow one to see the full length of her body. The man staring over Jenny's shoulder, who David had only met fleetingly once, was her husband, Simon.

Simon Rossington was a dark-haired stocky man in his mid-fifties who would not have been known for his attractiveness. Similarly, there was something about his demeanour and his facial expression that clearly indicated, to even a casual observer, that Simon Rossington would not be a man to be known for his intellect either. He very obviously portrayed a character that attempted to project the authority that only those who wish to be known as a bully project. He would not be someone found to be espousing with any knowledge, or any depth of intellect, on any topic of conversation more deeply than whether he thought he could "knock that blokes lights out", or conversely when discussions involved the opposite sex: the chances of "taking her home and fucking her stupid!"

The issue with Rossington that was easy to read from his stare, and thus potentially somewhat dangerous, was that he was totally oblivious to the fact that he had an intellect clearly embossed on his forehead saying "Stupid" and that his bully boy demeanour, could be disarmed by a petulant cat playing with a ball of wool.

Sadly, Rossington's egotistical nature caused him to believe that he was a man who, when he walked into a pub, turned heads, turned in subservient recognition, and that women got somewhat excited by his very presence. In fact, when he walked into a pub, he did turn heads, most usually, in dismay and a concerted hope that if one's eyes did not cross, then he would not attempt to engage in some banal self-centered conversation.

David turned back to Gordon. "Do you see the couple at the end of the bar? The woman is wearing tight white jeans, and the guy is the one whose eyes are piercing into the back of my head as I speak." Gordon averted his view to look over David's shoulder and smiled.

"Oh yes, I know that twat" Gordon said with a wry smile. "I've come across him in The Carlisle a few years back. He often comes up to say hello, Gordon, as if he knows me, but I have never had a conversation with him. But he is one of those blokes who thinks that just because he has said hello, in a pub a few times, he knows you. Not so long ago, he used to come into The Carlisle with a woman who must have been half his age, sporting her in a way that he wanted everyone to compliment him on his catch. But didn't realize that most of us thought, what an arse he must be, to be playing with a young girl as opposed to being with a woman more his age."

"Well, he's the husband of the woman who has made a complaint against me."

"Oh, ok, well, as I say, I don't know him beyond him talking to me as if he wants me to befriend him. He knows my name, but I haven't got a clue what he's called. Where do they live?"

"In Burton-on-Aire," David said.

"So why are they coming over here for a beer? There are plenty of decent pubs in Burton, for goodness sake." Gordon asked considerately.

"They may have come across for a meal," David offered.

"Well, all I can say, David, is that he has some interest in you, mate, as he has been staring in your direction for the last 10 minutes without flinching. What does he do?"

"I don't know exactly. I think he was in recruitment until his previous wife caught him shagging his secretary. Then, in order to pay her off in the divorce settlement, he had to resign from the agency and now is "project managing" works on a house that his wife purchased before they got married. It's not a house that they are going to live in. It's an investment, but she is concerned that he could take half her money and the house will not get finished if he walks away, if it all goes tits up with the marriage."

"Hmm, well, he looks like a bloke that would put pressure on her if he felt that he had her compromised in any way," Gordon smiled.

"I think you're right. But if they got divorced, I do not think he could get hold of any of her cash, as I believe that the marriage has to have lasted at least two years for there to be that sort of financial liability of sharing of personal assets." David said.

At that point, Gordon excused himself to go to the toilet. Being at the bar by himself, David turned to look towards the Rossingtons at the other end of the bar. Co-incidentally, Jenny was not visible, so David found himself peering straight towards Rossington's stare. Rossington gestured with his hand across his chest, making the sign of a cross. David smiled at him, totally bemused at Rossington's mentality.

Rossington repeated this demonic gesture four or five times until his wife returned. David just smiled back.

"Alright, mate?" Gordon asked as he returned from the toilet.

"I can't believe that daft idiot at the end of the bar. Coincidently as you went to the loo, she also went. When I looked at him, he made a repeated sign of the cross across his chest and gave me a demonic look in his eyes." David smiled, somewhat bemused.

"Why are they coming over here to drink? There are a number of decent pubs to drink at in Burton, and all within walking distance for them, I would have thought," Gordon posed.

"Oh, I agree, Gordon, but I sense that he is a control freak and very aggressive also and has taken offence that he thinks that his woman has been unfaithful and been with another bloke. I think that he feels that he is applying pressure on me and making me feel uncomfortable. Instead, what he is doing is indicating what a very sad little bastard he is, by choosing to drive over here, just in the hope that he might find me in here and unnerve me by doing so".

"Yeah, very sad, but that's how some people can be," Gordon agreed.

*****

A fortnight later, David had dropped into the Bulls Head for a quick pint with Gordon before going off to meet friends for a dinner party.

Half an hour after David had left the pub, Gordon was standing at the bar in his usual Friday night spot, talking to a number of the other regulars whilst eyeing up the various women who had ventured into the bar.

Unbeknown to Gordon, Rossington entered the bar with two men.

Rossington scanned the bar and saw Gordon at the end of the bar, waiting to be served another pint of Guinness. Gordon was so much a regular at the Bulls Head that he had his Guinness served in a particular shaped glass, distinct from anyone else who ordered a pint. It was not his own glass, as was very common years previously, before the onset of the Aids virus, when particular regulars had their own glass sitting, in pride of place on a back shelf behind the servery. No, it was a particular long thin pint glass that narrowed, mid-height, as if mimicking a woman's waist. Gordon believed that a Guinness tasted much better when more of the beer was able to touch the sides of the glass.

On lifting his pint from the bar, Gordon felt a tap on his right shoulder. Due to his omnipresence in the pub throughout the night (he was often there from 6.30 in the evening, having been dropped off by a taxi from work, as he had never learnt to drive, until closing time. It would not be unknown for him to drink 14 pints per night on a Saturday and Sunday night), and it was not uncommon for Gordon to be greeted by many people coming into the pub. Gordon turned around half smiling, expectant of being greeted by a variety of young women, who, seeing him in his Saville Row suit, would take the opportunity to compliment him on his suit, as a way to break the ice.

On rotating, Gordon came face to face with Rossington, whose stocky, relatively short posture was emphasized against Gordon's tall, elegant stance.

"Alright, Gordon," Rossington said in a harsh clipped tone.

Before Gordon could respond with any form of greeting, Rossington said," You've chosen the wrong friend there, Gordon, you really have!"

Smiling and somewhat bemused, Gordon responded, "Sorry mate, I have no idea what you're talking about. I hardly know you. In fact, I don't know you at all, beyond saying hello in a pub. We have never had a conversation, and with any respect due, I have no desire, or reason to enter into a conversation with you now." At which point Gordon turned to take another sip from his Guinness.

"I saw you talking with that fucking Roseman bloke the other week, and as I said, Gordon, you've chosen the wrong friend, mate. You really have." Rossington said aggressively.

"I really do not know who you are or who you think you are, mate, but if you do not leave me alone, I will have a word with the manager and get you thrown out," Gordon responded, getting more than a little annoyed at the imposition on his evening, by a very unpleasant and aggressive bloke, who he did not know.

Rossington turned, and in what was now quite a crowded bar, Gordon thought he had left the bar.

A few seconds later, however, Rossington came back with the two big burly beefs who had entered the pub with him, one on each shoulder towering over Rossington. The two men would, in 1980's parlance, have been described as being built "like brick shit houses".

Rossington turned to each of the heavies and, in a very melodramatic voice, said, "Remember his face, boys, remember his fucking face" He then turned and left the bar with his two hired friends.

The manager who had observed the events of the previous couple of minutes leant across the bar and addressed Gordon. "Are you alright, Gordon?"

"Yeah, no worries, Ian. Thanks, mate," Gordon responded calmly.

"Who the hell was that Gordon?" the manager asked in a quizzical and concerned manner.

"Oh, some screwed-up knob who does not know how to keep his wife in check," replied Gordon.

On leaving the pub, Rossington handed each of the Kelbrook heavies £30 as had been agreed previously, and the three men went their separate ways.

Rossington drove home contented that, in his mind, he had frightened Gordon, such that he would refrain from any future friendship with David. He parked his car on the driveway and, as he walked towards his front door, noticed Jenny sitting in the partially lit front room watching television.

He put his key in the door and entered the house. He walked straight upstairs without going into the lounge and sat on the bed in the spare room.

Since the events that had occurred at the Belfry, the two newlyweds had not shared a bed and had hardly spoken to each other when in the house at the same time. The tension was palpable. However, despite treating her with disdain and total disregard, Rossington would text Jenny and demand that she cooked him the dinner that he stipulated, and also the time that he would be home and wanted to eat it. When he had presumed that she had had sufficient time to have cooked his food, he would arrive home, come into the kitchen without a word of greeting, and stand in an imposing way, until his wife had served up his dinner. He would remove the necessary cutlery from the drawer beside the oven, pick up his dinner and take it upstairs to the spare room, all in total silence. Once he had completed his meal, he would return the plate to the kitchen table and leave it for his wife to put in the dishwasher, or wash up at the sink.

In an attempt to control his wife, Rossington had informed her that if he was to divorce her, he would be eligible to half the value of the property that his wife owned in Silkmoor.

Jenny had noticed that, since returning from The Belfry, the work being done at the house had slowed down dramatically. Tradesmen, who previously were on site daily, were often not in attendance at all. When querying where they were, Jenny was often told that they had an emergency job elsewhere. Rossington was the sort of man to enjoy applying psychological pressure on his wife and others to increase his almost psychopathic control over them.

Jenny had purchased the house, whilst she was single, as an investment, and had, at the time, agreed that Simon could project manage the job, even though he had no previous experience. In the current climate, she would have much preferred to have been in sole control of the project. She even contemplated moving into the house, in its current state, so as to give time and space between them. One of the reasons that she did not do that was because it would become clear to the workmen, that there was something going on in their relationship. Also, most of the men seemed to have known Rossington before taking the job, and Jenny was slightly paranoid that, in a location in which she was unknown, the bad word generated by local provisional gossip was probably not what she wished for now. Also, although her gut had been telling her, even before she had married Rossington, that she was doing the wrong thing, she felt that throwing in the towel, less than three months after marrying him, would give her a sense of total failure. As yet, she had not computed that, on occasion, it was better to hold one's hand up and admit the error of one's ways at the earliest, as opposed to rumble on, causing greater animosity to fester and waste time as time passed by unfulfilled.

*****

Throughout the following 12 months, David had regular telephone and email communications with Josephine, interspersed with occasional meetings at her practice's lavish offices in the centre of Manchester. On each occasion that David visited the legal practice, he was amazed at the scale of the premises, the number of large meeting rooms that fed off the voluminous reception area, that never had anyone in them.

The Reception Desk was large enough to service at least five receptionists, and the number of chairs in the waiting area could cater for a couple of cricket teams, their support staff, and most of their family members, should respite from bad weather at the nearby Old Trafford Cricket Ground be necessary.

The air that the legal firm wished to project from the layout and scale of its offices was one of opulence and prestige. In fact, the image that any casual visitor would actually perceive was of a company utilizing their exorbitant scale of fees, to spend a considerable majority of their income on needless and underutilized office space.

David had long realized that the main reason that solicitors charged highly inflated fees was not that it reflected their competence, but instead, it was a manner by which to make clients believe that if they were paying a large fee for something, it commensurately followed that the quality of service was also good. This same philosophy had been adopted throughout the retail industry for many, many years. David vividly remembers a friend who had worked in a soap manufacturing factory in Liverpool as his first job, telling him that the price of the most expensive soap at the factory gate was £0.28p. However, the various retailers they supplied to would charge their customers anything from £ 1.50 to £12.75 for the very same bar of soap.

A patient who was the director of a company local to Silkmoor, who had made a fortune out of hair straighteners, had once told David that their product was no better than a similar product from a competitor that was selling for a third of the price. However, the perception of the public was that, just because they were spending a considerable amount more money, the product must have been that much better. The same bullshit in public relations had always been inherent in the legal world too.

For some reason, the timeframe that legal matters take seems to be out of parity with the reality, with which other matters in life are addressed, the medical world accepting perhaps. The consequence is that, despite there being a well-defined protocol for a plaintiff submitting a formal complaint, the defendant responding, the plaintiff responding to the defendant's initial comments, and supposedly the defendant having the final say; in this situation, the plaintiff wrote four responses, causing the defendant to have to do similar.

The time allowed for each protagonist to respond to the commentary of the other was 28 days. The result was that over seven months passed without anything meaningful progressing.

David answered the telephone in his clinic on a bright mid-May morning.

"Hi David, it's Josephine. I hope you are well! Have you heard anything from the Investigating Committee yet?"

"Hi Josephine, yes I am fine, thank you. No, I have not, and I am hoping not to. If you recall, I stipulated that the CBUK send all correspondence directly to you, as I do not want to be distracted by receiving yet another frustrating letter from the CBUK whilst I am in the middle of the clinic!" David replied.

"Oh yes, I do recall those directions. My apologies." Josephine responded. David did not feel immensely comforted by the fact that his solicitor, and thus his legal lifeline to most probably being able to continue to practice in the future, had forgotten a simple agreement made only two months previously.

"Oh, okay, well I have received correspondence from the CBUK Investigating Committee, and they have stated that, from the nature of the complaint, there are grounds to proceed to investigate this matter further, with the resultant being a Professional Conduct Committee Hearing occurring at some stage in the future," Josephine stated succinctly, bluntly and without any emotional consideration for the information that she was imparting.

That said, being very skeptical as to the intent of the CBUK, David was not expecting the Investigating Committee not to wish to take it further, but the manner by which Josephine had delivered the coup de gras, could have been somewhat more sympathetic.

The whole way that the CBUK was set up, right from the directions of the very first Registrar, Mavis Cavendish, in 1994, clearly defined that the CBUK would always presume that the chiropractor was guilty, of any and every charge, and that the patient's intent was always without blemish or acrimony.

At the inception of the CBUK, they had chosen to charge each registrant £1000 per annum just to be on the Chiropractic Register. The reason given for such a huge subscription was so that the CBUK could create a "War Chest," just in case they were sued by any third party. Why they could not take out insurance, like any other company, institution, or individual, to cover the risk of being sued was never explained. Of course, perhaps the fact that they chose to house their headquarters in a prestigious building on Wimple Street in London may have had something to do with it.

Chapter 11 – The Investigation

Following notification from the Investigating Committee that there was a case to answer, the proactive period of attempting to substantiate the "facts" provided in the initial witness statement now commenced.

The Investigating Committee requested the original patient notes that related to the patient interaction between Jenny Dolton and Silkmoor Chiropractic Clinic. (For clarification, the CBUK where acting for the patient, who, at the time of being treated at Silkmoor Chiropractic Clinic, was not married and hence would be referred to by her maiden name of Dolton and not her current surname of Rossington).

The New Patient Form used by Silkmoor Chiropractic Clinic was derived from the standard new patient form produced by the main chiropractic association, the English Chiropractic Association. The form comprised eight A4 pages. The first two pages were filled out by the patient, and the following four pages were filled out by the chiropractor during the initial consultation, the history taking, and the examination. The final two pages were utilized for the clinician's notes, pertinent to each patient treatment visit.

The construction of the form used A3 pages, printed double-sided, folded in the middle, and stapled along the central crease with two staples.

The forms were sent to Peterson Forensic Laboratories in Marlow, near Oxford, to ascertain whether the entries on the form were chronological, and also to assess whether the form had been tampered with in any way. The laboratory was able to assess whether the staples had been removed or whether there was any disparity between the inks used on the form, or whether the dates that the treatment entries were stated to have been the case, were actually so. Quite a forensic investigation, more regularly used in serious police incidents, than in issues of professional medical misconduct matters, or so one might think.

Most of the accusations tabled by Jenny Dolton could be refuted if the new patient form was deemed to be authentic.

She stated that she continued to receive treatment after she returned from her honeymoon. However, the forms stated that she had been discharged 10 days before she flew out for her honeymoon. She stated that she had not been discharged following her announcement at the reception desk that after meeting David, she was not sure if she should continue with her wedding. She stated that she had had many more treatments than appeared on the treatment form.

If the forensic team agreed with the authenticity of the form, that it had not been tampered with, and that the entries were correct, not only would the accusations made, that could be refuted by the entries on the form be nullified, but it would also bring into severe doubt the sincerity of the accusations; that flowers had been bought and presented to Dolton; and it would even question the purported kiss in the consultation room during a treatment.

From posting the original forms to the Investigating Committee to receiving notification of the laboratory findings, three long weeks passed. David continued in the clinic with his growing and supportive patient base, but every time a patient, who was always enquiring in a considered way, asked how the investigation was going, he would allow his mind to conject that the forensic team would find something untoward with the form.

The fact that there was nothing untoward to find, did not comfort a mind that, for understandable reasons, allowed itself to get caught up in all sorts of irrational theories, and hence a degree of paranoia too.

The normal post arrived at the clinic at around 10.00 am to 10.15 am each morning. In usual situations, David would often hear the post drop onto the floor in the entrance lobby the moment the postman had put the post through the letterbox. On 16th July at 10.08 am., there was a knock on the clinic's front door. David excused himself from his patient and went to open the clinic door. Unsurprisingly, the postman handed over the majority of the post but held back one A4 brown envelope.

"One to sign for, I'm afraid." the postman said with a smile.

David knew that every envelope that required a signature on the receipt was a document sent from the CBUK. The psychological issue he had to contend with was that he now had a full patient list until lunchtime at 1.00 p.m. and therefore could only anxiously deliberate as to what the envelope contained.

The postman offered up a small digital tablet with what could only be described as a small thin black stick attached to it, with a small gauge lead coiled in the same way that telephone leads are coiled, between the handset and the phone receiver. Why anyone was ever asked to sign for something in such a manner, when it was impossible to enter a viable or legible signature, was beyond David. However, he dutifully offered up a squiggle on the screen with the black stick. The postman peered at the screen as if to authentic the signature and, once satisfied, handed over the envelope and said his goodbyes.

David placed the envelope and the rest of the post on the top of the Victorian radiator that covered the predominant part of one wall, in the entrance lobby and went back to attend to his patient.

"Apologies Mrs. Appleby. The postman wanted me to sign for an envelope." David said as he walked back into the treatment room, went across to the sink, and washed his hands before returning to complete the soft tissue work on Mrs. Appleby's right elbow. Mrs. Appleby had been a regular patient of David's since the clinic opened some 13 years previously. She was a very keen tennis player, and consequently, most of her musculoskeletal presentations related to her activity on the court. However, as one might expect, someone who had attended for treatment, often on a monthly basis, for such a long time had become a friend, by the mere fact that she had been aware of the birth of David's second child, and the growing up of both children, from nappies, through school, and had been a patient during the unfortunate period of David's divorce.

Mrs. Appleby had been kind enough to write a two-page handwritten letter to the Fitness to Practice Panel. She was one of 17 patients, 12 of whom had been female, who had readily responded immensely positively, when David had asked if they would mind writing a letter of support, that could be presented to the panel.

Angela Appleby had been a magistrate sitting in Bradford for a number of years, and was very vociferous in her condemnation of the nature of the accusation and the manner by which the investigation was being undertaken.

"Have you heard any more about the investigation?" asked Angela, as David wiped the residue of the aqueous cream off her elbow.

'Well, I am presuming that the letter that I have just signed for is from the CBUK, and so it will be interesting to see what unfolds from that." David said somewhat forlornly.

"I am so sorry that you're being put through all this ludicrous, vexatious victimization David. I do hope that the truth will come out, and justice will soon prevail, and that you will be able to put the whole of this sad, unnecessary ridiculous scenario behind you soon." Angela said with a smile, as she touched David softly on his arm as they left the treatment room.

The morning continued, one patient following another until Mr. Wakefield left the clinic at just after 1.00 p.m.

Whilst the kettle was boiling for a cup of lunchtime tea, David opened the seal on the A4 envelope. Inside was a covering letter and a stapled document. The title page of the document enclosed read "Forensic Analysis of Jenny Dolton's New Patient Form."

The document extended to eight pages of analysis and conclusions. David quickly scanned the first six pages until he reached the conclusion.

" It is our opinion, having undertaken an extensive forensic investigation and evaluation of the New Patient Form, that it was not tampered with in any manner in its composition. The staples appear authentic and original. There is absolutely no evidence that staples have been removed, altered, or amended."

"Due to the nature of the close proximity of the entry dates of each of the treatment notes, it is not possible to date each entry independently of another. There is no technology in existence to effectively carbon date entries when the entries are only a few days apart. That said, there is nothing about any of the entries to surmise that they are not all legitimate and authentic entries."

"Analysis of the handwriting indicates that, in the part of the form that was under the direction of the clinician Dr. David Roseman to fill in, there is unequivocal evidence that all these entries were made by the same hand."

"Analysis of the handwriting in the part of the form filled out by the patient Ms. Dolton, it is clear that this has been completed by someone other than the chiropractor, and from the samples that have been received of Ms. Dolton's handwriting and her signature, it is clear that the signature on the form was written by Ms. Dolton."

In conclusion, it is our professional opinion that the form that has been presented to us for analysis is a genuine, authentic, and original form and that everything entered on the form was done chronologically and without any amendments or alterations."

David emitted a very audible sigh on reading the conclusions. Even though he knew that everything on and in the form was genuine and authentic, and that the findings could not have been concluded in any other fashion; when one is under investigation and when matters are somewhat down to opinion, there is always the possibility of the opinion not reflecting the facts. Also, this was the first piece of information that seemed to have favoured him in almost 18 months, since he had received the initial complaint.

David felt totally relaxed and very relieved during his afternoon clinic, feeling that his stance had been exonerated and the lies that Dolton had told would now undermine her and her case. That evening he went to the pub to catch up with Gordon and give him the good news about the report.

*****

The CBUK contacted Blunton Lodge Hotel to request any details related to the spa treatment and a booking for lunch at the Hotel on Wednesday, 13th June 2016.

Blunton Lodge Hotel is a Spa Hotel on the periphery of Harrogate in North Yorkshire. The original property was built in 1740, the funds for which had been generated initially from the Slave Trade, and then income had been sustained via ownership of two large coalmines just East of Wakefield. The current owners had their stated aim of creating the most luxurious spa in the UK.

155

Rosemary Parkinson was the general manager who was asked to confirm the booking of Ms. Dolton for a spa treatment on Wednesday, 13th June 2016. When she checked the diary, Rosemary recalled that she had been at the front desk that lunchtime and recalled a very attractive man arriving with a similarly attractive woman. She recalled being slightly envious of the woman. Rosemary, who had worked her way up through the management structure at Blunton Lodge, was a local girl. When she first applied for a job, her desire was to meet one of the sous chefs and perhaps become romantically attached. However, as she had worked her way up through the management system, she had believed that her initial desires and expectations were now beneath her. Being the General Manager of one of the most prestigious hotels in Yorkshire, she had dreamt that perhaps one of the wealthy patrons might take her fancy. In the seven years that Rosemary had worked at Blunton Lodge, she had not gone out with any of the staff, or anyone connected with the hotel, but that did not mean that she was not constantly on the lookout for the right patron. She was not totally sure what she was looking for but felt that she would know when she saw or met him.

For that reason, Rosemary always cast an inquisitive eye over all the patrons, particularly the ones that she thought might be single. She had prided herself over the years in assessing which men were single, which were just having some fun with their secretaries, and which were attached or married to the woman with whom they were enjoying their time at Blunton Lodge. Her greatest test was attempting to work out whether the wedding rings that the men were wearing were pertinent to the partners they were with, or whether they were just a smoke screen, only implying that the couple were married. Of course, there was actually no way of resolving her thoughts, as it would have been more than her job was worth, to ask such direct questions that would ensure the necessary categoric answers. But even so, it did not stop her from playing the game in her own head.

For some reason, she had assumed that David and Jenny were not an affirmed couple. She was not sure exactly what the situation was. Perhaps they were just good friends, and Mr. Roseman was just treating Jenny to a birthday treat or something.

Consequently, when the letter requesting information in relation to the events that happened at Blunton Lodge on Wednesday, 13th June 2016, Rosemary Parkinson was able to recall the day quite well.

Rosemary responded to the CBUK, informing them that Mr. Roseman had rung them up on the morning of 13th June to ask if he could book a treatment for a lady late morning or at lunchtime that day. Reception had put Mr. Roseman through to the Spa Reception, where fortuitously, they had had a cancellation for a head and neck massage. Mr. Roseman consequently booked and paid for the appointment over the phone.

Rosemary Parkinson was able to confirm the payment, made by a personal debit card, and could also confirm that the lady had attended the appointment.

One thing that caused David a degree of concern, in principle more than in fact, once he became aware that Blunton Lodge had provided all the answers to the CBUK questions, related to GDPR and data protection. Why did Blunton Lodge freely offer the information requested, without first confirming with the pertinent client, that the information requested was pertinent to release? The CBUK is not the Police, it's powers of investigation are in no way as invasive as that of the Police, and consequently, they do not have the same authority to question anyone beyond the registrants, who are registered under their auspices.

It would probably end up being an academic point of discussion, but had the Blunton Lodge Hotel breached the data protection rights of David Roseman? If so, what sort of compensation could he claim?

Should he have a desire too, particularly if the resultant of the case caused a detrimental effect on his income long term?

*****

Some of the incidental matters that required substantiation related to the purchase of flowers within the clinic. Jenny stated that flowers were purchased specifically for her and left on the treatment bench for her. Conversely, David stated that the clinic regularly purchased flowers for both the reception and his treatment room. Unfortunately, on one occasion that David had picked up the flowers from the florist at lunchtime, he had not had time to put them in vases before Jenny had arrived for the first appointment of the afternoon. Consequently, he had left them wrapped up on his desk in his treatment room, and Jenny had misunderstood that they were for her when she was left in the treatment room to change.

When the clinic had 11 clinicians, all the day-to-day petty cash receipts were dealt with and logged by Lucy, the practice manager. For a period when David was severely depressed after his marriage break up, and he was the only clinician working at the practice, there was little coordination to any financial matters, let alone things like petty cash receipts. Fortunately, in the last eighteen months, he had adopted a system that logged all incidental payments. Consequently, he was able to submit regular payments to the florist before, during, and after Jenny Dolton had been a patient.

Following the CBUK request for receipts for regular purchases of flowers for the clinic, David has been able to send weekly receipts for two bunches of flowers since April 2015. On sending the information, David felt reassured that he had been able to once again refute another of the accusations tabled by Jenny Dolton.

Throughout the period of investigation, there was an underlying disease felt by David Roseman. Here was his governing body, the body to whom he paid a substantial annual subscription, and consequently, was a contributor to the existence and running of this organization, desperately looking to discredit him as a professional. To find any means possible to prove him guilty of acts that one patient out of most probably eight thousand patients who had received treatment from him, stated had occurred. The very existence of the Fitness to Practice Hearing that Jason Brownley had stated usually resulted in a temporary suspension, even before the facts had been investigated, let alone verified, clearly illustrated to David that he had to prove himself innocent, as opposed to the CBUK having to find him guilty. The burden of proof seemed to have been taken as assured merely from the fact that a patient had made a complaint. The fact that, during the initial transfer of statements, between the plaintiff and the defendant, there had been clear illustrations, not only of inaccuracies in the plaintiff's story but blatant fabrications of lies, and then blatant alteration of commentaries that in previous statements, had been stated and unequivocally signed, did not cause any reasonable adjudicator, to question, let alone throw out the case, compounded David's belief that the system was prejudiced.

There pervaded a concept that it was important that the CBUK find a certain amount of their registrants guilty of gross professional misconduct in order that they were then seen as a creditable organization. Of course, the fact that there were relatively few chiropractors practicing in the country, and thus a very minimal number of complaints referred to the CBUK in the first place, made the need to "set an example," irrespective of the gravitas of the complaint, all the more compelling.

*****

159

On 28th September, the clinic phone rang. "Hi David, it's Josephine. How are you?" Josephine always attempted to start the interaction with David in a very bright, upbeat manner, irrespective of the information that she was about to impart. The fact that she called at all indicated that something major had happened, or was just about to happen.

"Hi Josephine, fine, thank you, how are you? I sense you have something to impart," David responded in a mildly resigned fashion. This case, from its inception, had been ongoing for over a year now, and even though he knew that, in his mind, he had done nothing wrong, there was always the "what if" scenario. The "what if" the panel chose to make an example of him, which resulted in him being suspended from practice for a period. If that happened, even if the suspension was only for a short period, due to the tight-knit community in which he was located, it would be the death nail for his practice.

He tried manfully not to allow his mind to wonder, such that multiple "what if" scenarios, all of which were negative, resulted in him becoming downhearted and even mildly depressed.

"We have received notification from the CBUK of the date of the Professional Conduct Committee Hearing. It will commence on Monday 6th November. Now I suggest that you book the whole week out of the clinic that week, as the case will definitely last the whole of that week, and it may be wise to book out the early part of the following week, as it could even go into the following week."

"You are kidding me. You really are kidding me, aren't you? How the hell can something like this go on for a fortnight? Bloody murder trials can take less time, for Christ's sake. It smells to me that someone is milking the system."

"I can tell that you're frustrated, David, and I am sure that I would be too, but I have to give you the worst-case scenario so that you can prepare for it!" Josephine responded in her best bedside manner tone.

"Now that we have a date, we need to organize a meeting with your barrister so that he can brief you, in regards to the process and procedure of these types of hearings, and also to make sure that we have all the information necessary to formulate our argument. The barrister that we have commissioned is called Malcolm Finsbury. Malcolm has a very distinguished CV and, for many years, was the chief prosecuting counsel for the General Medical Council. So he knows his way around this type of law very comprehensively and will be the best man for the job David". Josephine stated reassuringly.

"So, how many CBUK cases has he defended?" David asked cautiously.

"This will be his first David," Josephine responded in a slightly clipped voice.

"Oh! So he has spent years acting for the prosecution of another organization, and now he will be acting for the defense for the first time in front of another organization. I am not sure how I feel about that, Josephine!" David responded.

"How do you mean David?" Josephine asked pointedly.

"Well, I would imagine that although, in principle, dealing with a professional conduct hearing would be similar between two professional bodies, and perhaps the fact that both are medical may add to the similarities. But is it that easy to go from Prosecution to Defense, and if it is, why do most barristers seem to stay on one side of the fence and not oscillate from side to side more frequently?" David posed eloquently.

"I hear what you say, David, but the fact that Malcolm Finsbury has spent a lot of time on the prosecution side of professional

161

misconduct cases, would have given him a very good understanding as to how prosecutors think and what aspects of the pertinent law they would focus on. I actually think, knowing the experience that he has attained over the years, that he really is the perfect man for the job. Also, the fact that this will be his first case dealing with and in front of the CBUK will stimulate him more than another GMC case. Anyway, when would you be available to meet him to go through the initial briefing, please?"

"Well, as you know, Wednesdays are my day off, and therefore any Wednesday would suit my diary. It would have to be in the morning, though, as I pick my son up from school on a Wednesday, and I would not wish to alter that routine." David said.

"Fine, I am sure that we can arrange something on a suitable Wednesday morning for you," Josephine said reassuringly.

"Where is he based, Josephine?" David asked.

"He's based in Manchester. His chambers are just off Albert Square if you know it? Not far from the Town Hall."

"No, I don't know it specifically, but my ex-wife's parents lived in Manchester, and so I know the main areas like Deansgate, etc., so it won't be difficult to find. So ideally for me, any time around 10-11.00 would suit, as I imagine we will be a couple of hours, and that will give me ample time to get back to Beachford to pick up my son." David said, in a fashion that assured Josephine that, as best as possible, the meeting time would be diarorised to suit him as the client, not the barrister.

David was aware that those in the legal profession, similar to those in the medical profession, had a perception of their importance to society well in excess of their actual relevance. Each level of the legal system showed each other an over-pompous deference to each other. David knew that, as the briefing solicitor, Josephine would address

162

Malcolm Finsbury as "Mr. Finsbury" and not Malcolm, during each meeting, in a vane attempt to maintain his ivory tower status. Again, like the vast majority of the medical world, the legal profession failed to realize that they were in a service industry, and that deference should always flow towards the person paying their fees, and not the other way around.

*****

Wednesday, September 13th, was a bright sunny day. The temperature was about 11 degrees when David got into his car, with his file full of documents, letters, and copies of emails, texts, and Whats App messages between himself and Jenny Dolton. The fact that the weather in Silkmoor was fine and sunny did not necessarily direct that the weather in Manchester would be anything similar, even though it was only about 40 miles away.

The drive to Manchester was uneventful, and the weather maintained being dry and sunny all the way along the route. The drive took David via the market town of Sippingdale and then along the A59 to Colne and then onto the M65 to Burnley and the M66 to Manchester. In all the time that David had travelled from Silkmoor to Manchester, which admittedly was more when he was married and visiting his in-laws in Prestwich, on the outskirts of the city, he was constantly amazed at the lack of traffic on the M65 and M66 motorways. He could not imagine that there were any other motorways in the whole of the UK that were so quiet, throughout every part of the day.

Not surprisingly, Craigland Chambers was located in a prestigious Edwardian property, in a quiet street, just off the northern end of Deansgate, which was the main tributary road in the centre of

Manchester. The building was set back from the main section of the street, facilitating end on parking in front of all the similar premises in the street. What a shame David had not been told that it was possible to park in front of the chambers. That would have saved him parking at the southern end of Deansgate and walking the 20 minutes to the chambers. The pavement was broad, and at the junction between the kerb and the road edge, plane trees had been planted every 10 metres. Thus, the impression of affluence pervaded along the street, a mere 100 metres from the hustle and bustle of the Deansgate thoroughfare.

The reception area reminded David of a 1980s architects office that he had worked in. A large, smoked glass coffee table was the focal element of the waiting area. The reception desk was a bespoke ash-veneered unit, which, unless the receptionist sat up totally erect, obscured her from the view of anyone walking into reception.

David made himself known to the receptionist and informed her that he was there to see Malcolm Finsbury. The receptionist, an attractive, dark-haired woman in her mid-twenties, wearing a fitted black dress, asked David to fill in the attendance book, which he duly did.

Once that formality was complete, she asked David to take a seat whilst she told "Mr. Finsbury" that he was here.

In the five minutes that David was in the waiting area, he scanned through the Craiglands Chambers Barrister brochure. There were 24 barristers who worked out of these chambers, across the whole spectrum of law, from family to commercial, criminal, corporate, professional indemnity, to professional conduct.

"David, good morning. Nice to meet you, Malcolm Finsbury. Follow me, please." Malcolm Finsbury said in a very pleasant, assured manner, as he greeted David with an outstretched arm on his arrival at the Reception.

"We will be in Conference Room 3 for the next cou,
Amanda, if you can make sure that it's booked out for that time, ...
could you bring in some coffee now, and some sandwiches in about
an hour, please?" Malcolm asked the receptionist with a warm smile.

Malcolm Finsbury was a man in his early fifties, of average height
for his age, who would be described as stocky if one was being polite
and somewhat portly if one was not. He clearly projected a
considered, warm demeanour, on a first meeting.

As David and Malcolm walked into Conference Room 3, David
was greeted by Josephine, who stood up from behind a bundle of lever
arch files.

"Hi, David, nice to see you. How are you?' Josephine said as she
offered her hand towards David.

Conference Room 3 was a not inconsiderable room with a
conference table, unsurprisingly as its centerpiece, surrounded by
twelve chairs. The room was mostly lit by daylight streaming in
through the two Georgian windows to the narrow end of the room.
Half a dozen semi-circular wall lights were equally placed on the
three remaining walls, offering a warm light bathing the cornices of
the walls.

Malcolm offered David the chair at the head of the rectangular
conference table, allowing David to cast his eye along the length of
the table and out through the windows on the opposite wall.

"So David, what this meeting is all about, is to first ascertain the
extent of all the facts. Now I know that you will have been through
them with Josephine at least a couple of times, but I need to
understand how you feel about everything that you are being accused
of. Hearing it from you, in your own words, and being in front of
you, and listening to you, I can get a sense of who you are and also an
idea of how you might act, should we choose to have you take the

stand at the hearing." Malcolm Finsbury said in a very articulate manner.

"Coffee David?" Josephine asked as she got up from the table.

"I'd prefer just to have some water if you don't mind," David responded with a smile.

Throughout the next two and a half hours, the whole story, from the initial telephone conversation in June 2016, through to the interaction at the side of the road a matter of weeks before, was outlined.

"Well, I am glad that we have gone through matters so comprehensively, David. It has indicated a number of things to me. First, you are a very eloquent, conscientious, and passionate man. Consequently, you would be very competent in front of a conduct committee, should we feel that it would be beneficial for you to take the stand. Secondly, you have the events that occurred during the consultations and treatments of Patient A very clearly structured in your mind". Malcolm Finsbury stated quite profoundly.

"Furthermore," Malcolm continued, "I can now tell you that I have read the various statements of Patient A and from the litany of endless contradictions, within the numerous statements that she has produced, each subsequent statement undermining substantially what, in previous statements were deemed to be indisputable facts, I am very surprised that the Investigating Committee has not discharged the complaint already, and instead, allowed things to progress to an actual hearing. However, this is the first case that I have been involved with the CBUK, and thus perhaps I am overlaying the experience I have had with the GMC and interpolating things, as I feel a similar investigating committee of the GMC would have acted. Sadly, each professional governing body acts in isolation from each and every other professional governing body, even the ones with similar associations, like the chiropractic and medical bodies."

166

"So, are you saying, Malcolm, that even though there is no direct correlation between two similar professional bodies, in regards to how they assess the seriousness of professional misconduct, at this stage, it would not be unreasonable to assume that if the GMC had thrown this case out, in the course of time, the CBUK would not unreasonably end up doing the same?" David asked, in an attempt to try and get some comfort from where someone, who had been involved in cases like this many times in the past, might think the resultant would be.

"Well, I understand the premise by which you raise that question, David, and in principle, it would not be unreasonable for there to be a universality of acceptability of conduct and also a strict correlation, between similar governing bodies as to how they would assess similar complaints. But sadly, not only is each governing body different, but also the manner by which two different investigating committees, within the same organization might adjudicate, can vary markedly," Malcolm responded with an apologetic smile.

"So, what you're saying is that there is an element of the lap of the Gods as to how this ends up?" David responded somewhat forlornly.

"Well yes and no. Clearly, there is the Code of Professional Conduct and professional guidelines that direct the various committees. But very rarely do the specifics of any case categorically, or as you would say in your profession, pathognomonically, conform to the particular clauses of a Code of Conduct or professional conduct guidelines. Thus, there will always be the predicament that any decision is based on the interpretation of those sitting on the committee. To that extent, the outcome of the Professional Conduct Committee Hearing will be very much dependent on the personality of the panel members and, in particular, the chairperson. So how we present, will be key to the outcome." Malcolm mentioned sanguinely.

"Hmm, I shall always remember being told, and also experiencing, when I was an architectural student, that presentation is key. Presentation is always as important as content, but often, even more important. I once remember completing the drawing up of the major design project for my degree year at my parents' home in the country. That allowed me to work all the time and allowed my mother to do all the cooking. I worked assiduously from Friday night through Saturday and Sunday, drawing up all the necessary drawings as directed by the brief. Once I had completed the plans, sections, and elevations, I relaxed, believing all my work was done. But before I went next door to watch some television and relax, I checked the brief to make sure I had complied with all the criteria for what one needed to present. To my shock and horror, I read that 20% of the overall mark was down to a model of the proposed building. I had not done a model, and my parents lived in the countryside, and there were no model shops for 35 miles. Even so, it was a Sunday evening, and no model shops would be open anyway. After I had completed cursing and rebuking myself for my oversight, I tried to think if there was anything in my parents' house that I could use. My logic was that if I did not produce any model, I could not get any of the 20% apportioned to the overall grade. However, if I produced something, I had to get at least 5%. My father was a builder, and he had a large carpentry shop. Could I go down and make something out of timber, I thought? No, it would take too long. Eventually, I went into the attic and found some of the Lego that I had loved as a child. I quickly cobbled together a small section of the building I had designed. Clearly not to the correct proportion, as I was directed by the size of the Lego bricks. The next day I hung up all my drawings in the presentation room with all my colleagues and placed my "model" on a chair in front of my drawings. The format of such an assessment was that initially, the tutors would choose three or four students to present their specific schemes, before making generalized comments to the whole year. After the students' presentations, the tutors talked about their favourite designs and their favourite drawings. Then, out of nowhere, one of the tutors said, *"Now, in relation to the models, ladies and gentlemen, I have to single out one in particular. This Lego by David Roseman shows inspiration, quirkiness, and a real ingenuity of expression in three dimensions and immense guts to do such a thing. Congratulations David."* And believe it or not, I got 15/20% for my model. So yes, I have a lot of experience in regards to the importance of presentation." David completed his story, smiling at the memory of that event some 30 years before. And even then, he could never have imagined bringing up the story, in conversation with a barrister, whilst engaging in a professional conduct matter, either.

"Anyway, that said, Malcolm, from your experience of similar cases and from the content of this case, what do you feel will be the outcome here? Now I know you may wish to add plenty of caveats to your answer, but I am not interested in ifs, buts, and maybes. I am aware of all those. I just want you to give me your professional opinion of your prospects as to the outcome of this case, please," David said in a very polite but direct and mildly forceful manner.

"Yes, accepting all the caveats, the main issue here is that she has clearly lied, time and time again, and therefore should be seen to have little credibility. The nature of your business is that, in situations where there is some sort of dispute, it is always one person's comments against another person's comments. He said, she said. It is impossible for that not to be the case, as you cannot expect to provide chaperones for every patient, as that would be not only prohibitively expensive to the clinic, but also a potential breach of a patient's privacy and privilege. Similarly, you cannot install CCTV cameras in the treatment rooms, as that would cause potential criticism of breach of patient confidentiality and could also lead someone to say that there was unnecessary voyeurism. So, you work in a very difficult situation where you are, particularly as a male chiropractor, at risk of someone falsely accusing you of something inappropriate. But all that said, the only thing that is at issue is the timeframe from you discharging the patient, to when you met her socially. Now I accept the reasons why the timeframe was so short, and there is great validity in what you did, and personally, I believe you did what you did, when you did, for the altruistic reasons that you have stated. However, part of the issue will be that most of the people who may be assessing your actions, and adjudicating your decision process, will not be similarly caring or altruistic and, thus, will not give credibility to the reason for the timing being as it was." Malcolm smiled somewhat wryly.

"But surely the chronology of events meant that, if I was to be at all altruistic and my intent at all meaningful and helpful, the window in which I had to assist was what it was. Also, in doing a good deed, is anyone going to be directed by assessing whether the timing of doing that deed would be the subject of a professional misconduct hearing, at the time of looking to enact that good deed? No, of course not," David responded.

"Anyway, all that said, I believe that things fall in your favour 80 to 20." Malcolm smiled.

"Well, that is probably an appropriate place at which to wind it up for today, is it not," David said as he stood up from the conference table.

Josephine and Malcolm smiled and almost simultaneously stood up, collected up their loose papers, replaced them into their matching flame red lever arch files, and put them under their arms, at the same time offering their hands to David.

When David turned his mobile phone on leaving the chambers, he noticed a message from his son, saying that he wanted to get the train back from school, instead of being picked up. This usually meant that there had been a fun interaction at school with his schoolmates that he wished to continue, or be part of on the train home. Thus, not being in a rush to get back to Silkmoor, David decided he would browse around this part of Manchester. On his walk here, he noticed that this was clearly the commercial office part of Manchester, and not only were there new buildings going up, but also most of the other buildings in the area were also relatively new. He walked back to Albert Square, which was surrounded by a number of bars and a couple of restaurants, and had tables and chairs outside, to optimize the south-facing aspect of the square.

David had not realized how long his meeting had taken, and when he looked at his watch, he realized how fortunate it had been that his son had chosen to go home by train, as David would never have got back in time to pick him up anyway. David chose to sit on a rustic bench outside a Bavarian-styled pub to contemplate his current predicament. Once he had appraised the conference meeting he had just had, he decided that, even though he was driving, he could treat himself to one beer.

On coming back into the square with his beer in hand, David cast his eye around the people mingled in the square. The way that everyone was dressed, they were clearly all office workers and predominantly in their mid-twenties to mid-thirties.

David was not aware whether this was a skill that he had always had, but he presumed that he had acquired it since becoming a chiropractor. That skill was the ability to recognize someone from behind, as easily as from the front. He had presumed that the skill had developed, due to the fact that the predominant time that he engaged with any of his patients, they were always lying face down. Thus subconsciously, he must have picked up on the nuanced identity features that availed the observer when looking at the back of someone. Either way, David had been able to recognize numerous friends and patients in this way. He allowed himself a wry smile as he perceived that, once again, he had identified someone he knew from behind. However, this person lived in Silkmoor, and David thought it would be very strange if he had happened upon Ian outside a pub, in a square in Manchester. Ian was someone that David had never had a conversation with, but had seen to raise a mutual hand to, or just to acknowledge, when the two of them dropped off or picked up, their respective children at Saint Barnaby's Primary School some years earlier.

Due to the unnatural environment in which he perceived to have found an acquaintance, he was very cautious to go up to this person, who he still had only seen from the back. David manoeuvred himself so that he could at least see this person in his profile.

"Ian, what an amazing surprise. How are you?" David said, offering his hand.

Ian turned, and partly in shock, he noticed and then recognized David and smiled, saying, "David, hi, I am well, thank you, how are you, and what brings you to Manchester?"

"Well, I was going to ask you the same thing, but even though I have seen you around often in Silkmoor, either at school, the cricket, or out on your bike, we have never had a conversation, so there should be no surprise that you might work in Manchester."

"Oh, no, I don't work in Manchester, I work in Leeds, but we have an office in Manchester, and tonight we are having a staff party, so this is as good a place to meet before we go off for a meal," Ian explained." So what are you doing over here? I thought your practice was in Silkmoor."

David told Ian the reasons for him being in Manchester and, without giving any details as to the specifics of the complaint, informed Ian of the fact that a female patient had made a certain unfortunate accusation against him.

"Oh, I am so sorry to hear that, David. That's really shit! God, there are some nutters around, aren't there?" Ian said in a conciliatory manner.

After a further short conversation, David chose to leave Ian to his Manchester work colleagues and wished him well for his evening.

On the drive home, David reflected on the warmth of emotion that Ian had offered so openly. Someone who could not really be called an acquaintance, but someone who had clearly heard of him professionally and who knew the reputation that David had within the town, since the clinic had opened some 15 years previously. Someone who had also said that if he had had a musculoskeletal issue, he had been told, by his cycling friends, that David was the person to go and see. David felt reassured that even someone who did not know him personally, clearly held him in high esteem. A very pleasant thought to redress the balance psychologically. After months of having been distracted by the efforts of someone, who was intent on destroying his reputation, and his business, following years of personal isolation and navel-gazing following his divorce, it was very uplifting to pick up on a sense of how others perceived him.

David realized on the journey home from Manchester that a small business does not survive in a town the size of Silkmoor for almost 15 years, without having a sound reputation and regard from the community it serves. That warmth of emotion comforted him for the remainder of the drive.

Chapter 12 – Towards the Hearing

October 10th was a bright, crisp autumnal morning. The leaves on the deciduous trees were in the process of turning and, in a number of cases, creating a plethora of amazingly vivid and varied shades of reds, yellows, and browns. David had had a busy morning, starting at 7.00 am, as was his want, so that he could see patients who worked in either Bradford or Leeds, before they left for work on the train from Silkmoor.

Having a short break between his initial group of patients and his mid-morning treatments to come, David chose to do a bit of housekeeping of the clinic and to take the used patient tissues and head rolls out to the bins.

The clinic was prominently located, on a sharp bend, on a tributary road exiting Silkmoor, within five minutes walk of the town centre.

Although on most occasions that David took rubbish to the bins at the back of the building, he would take the stairs to the basement and exit through the back door of the basement, on this particular day, he chose to enjoy the outside a short while longer, and left the clinic via the front door, to walk thirty yards along the pavement, before turning left, and then left again to access the yard behind the clinic, where the bins were housed.

As David was walking along the pavement beside the tributary road, a black, 5 series BMW came around the corner from the direction of the town centre. Even though there was no obstruction in the flow of the traffic, the car slowed down abruptly as it passed David. David recognized the car from its personalized number plate SR18 TIT, a number that few people would forget once they had seen it.

As he walked past the car, which had now stopped, despite being just beyond a blind bend, the front passenger window slid down, and he heard a soft, feeble female voice say, "Are you alright" in a very apologetic manner.

Jenny Dolton had, for some reason, chosen to drive past David's clinic, and on seeing him, instead of continuing to drive on, deliberately chosen to stop and attempt to engage with David in a manner that attempted to appear concerned. Yet this was the very woman who was currently attempting to ruin his reputation and his career.

David paused for a second, bent down such that he could look at her sitting in the driver's seat of the car, and then, without commenting, walked on. Jenny drove at the same pace as David was walking, until such time as she could pull her car slightly off the road at the junction with a side road that created a T-junction with the tributary road.

Once she was stationary and not blocking the traffic, Jenny Dolton leaned across from her driver's seat and said, "I am so sorry, but he made me do it. What can I do? I am worried that he could take my house away from me," Dolton clearly attempted to plead with David, for some understanding and forgiveness, for the predicament that she obviously believed was not of her making and for which she was the victim.

David, once again, bent forward so that he could see Jenny's face. Her eyes were apologetic, and David realized that she wanted him to forgive her, for the situation in which they both found themselves.

For almost a minute, David just stared, being both bemused and incredulous, as to how this woman could not comprehend what she had brought about, whether he should or should not respond, and in what way he should reply, if he deemed it correct, and appropriate to do so.

Being uncomfortable with the silence, Jenny chose to speak, "I am so sorry, I really am, but what can I do? What can I do to help you?"

David thought for a moment, and for every second that passed, his anger grew to such an extent that he realized that, although it would not be at all professional, he had to respond and respond as his anger directed him.

"How can you help me? How can you fucking help me?" he spat out, incensed at being asked such a stupid and banal question. "I will tell you how you can fucking help me. You can withdraw the complaint immediately and allow me to get back to living my own life, without the thought of you trying to ruin my reputation and my career. That is what you can do, and you can go home right now and do the right thing NOW!" David said angrily.

"But I can't. You don't know what he is like. He is a bully, and he is threatening me, if I do not go through with this," Jenny responded again in a feeble, apologetic tone.

"I don't give a shit who or what he is, he's your husband, and thus you need to tell him what is the right thing to do." David retorted.

"But you have no idea what he is like. You really don't. I am afraid of him and what he might do to me." Jenny pleaded once again.

"Listen, Jenny. I realized what he was like when I first met him, and from what you told me, before you went off and married him. I spent time with you, attempting to help you with what to do, but you chose to ignore that advice. Advice that, if you had taken it at the time, none of us would be in this shit now. So please do not expect me to have any compassion towards you for the predicament you freely put yourself in. All that I ask, as any decent person would ask, is that you do the right thing, and you know what the right thing is, and stop this right now!" David said.

Jenny looked at David for a moment, with an expression that again was begging for his forgiveness, and then, as she slowly wound the window up, said, "I wish I could help, I really do, but I can't. I really can't. I really can't. I'm too scared. I'm so sorry – take care!"

With that, she put the car in gear and drove away, peering back in her rearview window to check on the man she had realized for some time was the person that she would have much preferred to have been in a relationship, but felt trapped and uncertain and unable to amend anything. She realized that from almost the first moment that she had met David. It was the reason that she had baked him a dinner dish and delivered it on her second visit to the clinic. That is the reason, ironically, that she had sent David a photo whilst on her honeymoon of her in the bikini he had bought her.

As often happens, immediately after one has failed to act appropriately, within seconds of the car driving away, David remonstrated with himself for not turning his camera on his phone to video and record the interaction with Jenny Dolton, as he felt that this would have proved irrefutably damning evidence at the upcoming hearing.

*****

It was three weeks less than twelve months since the Fitness to Practice Hearing to the Professional Conduct Committee Hearing. As before, the Professional Conduct Hearing took place in the International Dispute and Resolution Building on Fleet Street.

Having been informed that the case would take at least a week and maybe two, David contacted his close friend Tom, who he had known from his days working as an architect in the West End of London. Tom Wickleby was one of those people who you might not speak to for almost a year, but when you did, within two minutes, the energy, atmosphere, and camaraderie were as if you had spoken to him daily for the last 9 months.

Tom and David first met on a cricket tour to Ireland. Back in 1989. Ireland was not known as a mecca for cricket tours, but Tom and David worked for a large design company whose managing director was a mad keen cricketer. He wasn't the best cricketer in the world, but that was one of the beauties of cricket - you did not have to be particularly good at it, to enjoy playing it. Geoffrey Woodcombe had run a successful design company for many years and had consequently made some strong business and social contacts around Europe. In 1989 Geoffrey celebrated his 50th birthday and chose to invite a number of his staff, who he knew played cricket, to go on a weekend tour to Dublin. The team was due to play two matches.

David had fortuitously become one of Geoffrey's favourites in the office. It was a large office housed across three buildings, in Soho Square and around Tottenham Court Road, in the West End of London. David did not come across Geoffrey in the day-to-day running of the office, as David worked in one of the satellite offices, and Geoffrey never came across to those offices for any reason. However, the year before the Dublin trip, David had put his name down to play in a cricket match for the company. David usually kept wicket, but as the company had a regular wicketkeeper, David started off in the slips to the faster bowlers, one of which was Tom Wickleby.

Once the fast bowlers had begun to tire, Geoffrey would bring himself on to attempt to "hold up an end." If one had asked Geoffrey over a pint what he bowled, he would say a variety of off-spin. In practice, all he bowled were long slow hops that any half-decent batsman, owning a pair of eyes, would pull off the middle and hit to the midwicket boundary for a six.

As luck would have it, in the first match that David played for Woodcombe's, when Geoffrey came on to bowl, David was taken from the slip cordon, to patrol the midwicket boundary. Earlier in his sporting career, David had played rugby at Wasps, predominantly as a full back, and thus was very adept at taking a high ball out of the sky, even though, mostly, that would be a rugby ball.

Wasps was one of the top rugby clubs in England at the time. When David played for them, they got to the final of the Pilkington Cup, which was the senior knockout cup in the country for three consecutive years. Ironically, each year they played Bath, and each year, despite starting the match with big leads, after a short period of time, they always ended up capitulating to Bath.

Wasps ran nine teams, so it was not necessarily a great achievement to say that one had played at Wasps. However, for part of one season, when David played at fullback, there was a period of time when the team sheet went up on a Thursday night after training where the 1st XV fullback was the current England fullback; the 2nd XV fullback would be the England fullback the season following and the 3rd XV fullback was David Rosman.

In the second over that Geoffrey bowled, he once again dragged the ball down short, effecting it to bounce up like a tennis ball. The batsman's eyes opened as if he had just received a massive dose of atropine, as he swung his bat through the ball, assured that he was in the process of hitting his first six of the season. The ball soared towards the midwicket boundary, which was the longest boundary on the pitch, for obvious reasons to attempt to give Geoffrey the greatest protection. David picked the ball out of the sky early and raced along the boundary to where he predicted it would fall, taking a comfortable catch in the process. Geoffrey became instantly elated. David had become a hero in his eyes in an instant, and David's status within the company had rocketed in a few seconds.

To ensure that he cemented his status, David went on to take three more catches off Geoffrey's bowling that afternoon, to give him his best bowling figures for years.

At the end of the match, Geoffrey made a beeline for David and ensured that he was set up with a few pints at the bar.

The result was that when the memo came out about the company cricket tour to Ireland, Geoffrey personally rang David, to not only make sure that he had received the memo, but also that he would be coming on the tour.

Flying out of Heathrow, a group of fifteen players, all members of the company, congregated at the Aer Lingus check-in desk. David did not recognize any of the others beyond Geoffrey and, thus, just stood on the periphery until their flight was called.

Arriving at a local country club in Dublin, everyone congregated in the hotel lobby awaiting to be allocated their rooms. Not unsurprisingly, as with all sports tours, whether at an amateur, professional, or international level, players are paired with a roommate. This is where David and Tom first met, as they were paired to share a room for three nights.

After sharing a number of beers with the rest of the squad, David and Tom retired to their room. Tom was on the board of Geoffrey's design company and had been a successful rugby player himself, eclipsing David by being chosen to play for London when the divisional championships existed. Tom was a very confident guy, and his inherent self-belief had allowed him to secure his place in his club rugby team, Richmond.

Within a short period of time, both David and Tom realised that they shared a lot in common. They were both only children. Both had slightly mad mothers; both had been sent to boarding school, and both had a passion for playing and watching sports, and both were immensely competitive in everything they did.

Their deep friendship, as it was to become, was cemented on that first weekend. In the following years, particularly when David moved to another design company, they may not see each other for months or even years, but as soon as they made contact, the banter returned instantly.

Tom's first marriage was to a woman whose parents lived in Zimbabwe, and thus the wedding was held in a small game park on the outskirts of Harare. The bond between David and Tom had grown such that Tom asked David to be his master of ceremonies at his wedding, which David took as a great honour.

The wedding had passed off extremely well. How could it not when the venue for the wedding breakfast was a marquee set on the outskirts of a game park where, stood inside the marquee, with the side wall canvasses removed, one's backdrop were leopards and tigers, gazelles and elephant,roaming in the game park a short distance beyond.

Although, at one point, David believed he had fallen foul of one of the guests. The meal was set up as a buffet, and one of David's jobs was to usher respective tables to the buffet tables, once they were free. The marquee was quite tight, and thus the space for movement between each table was difficult. At one point, when David was directing tables towards the buffet, a quite gruff-voiced gentleman called out to David from the back of the marquee.

"Excuse me, David," the man said in quite a loud clipped voice.

Presuming that the man was displeased at the time it was taking for his table to go to the buffet, David responded with a smile, "Sorry, Sir, your table is after this one."

"No, no, no," the man replied, a little more curtly in a strong Zimbabwean accent.

Believing the man to think that he should get priority, David once again informed the gentleman, slightly more forcibly, that his table would be the one after this.

"No, no, no," the man said once again. David was starting to get a little frustrated. By this point, David had managed to get somewhat closer to the gentleman's table so that he could hear him without the both of them shouting.

When David got to a point where they could hear each other talking normally, the gentleman introduced himself.

"Hi there, David. My name is Norman Donaldson. I am the airport manager at Harare airport," the man started.

Bully for you, David thought to himself. Why would this man spout off as to his job status, David thought. Tom's bride Marina had worked for a few airlines in Zimbabwe when she was growing up, and that is why a number of the guests were associated with the airline business.

"Listen, David," the man said again. "I've been very impressed with the way that you have run the show this afternoon," smiling as he said it.

"Oh, that's very kind of you. It has been a privilege to do it," David responded with a warm smile.

"Now, I imagine that you might be staying in the country for a while after the wedding, and I also presume that you will be flying back from Harare airport," Norman stated.

"Yes, both those assumptions are correct," David said, not knowing exactly where this conversation was going but still aware that he was effectively on duty and a representative of the married couple and had to maintain courtesy toward the guests at all times.

"Well, here is my card. When you arrive at the airport to fly home, make sure that you make yourself known to me, please." Norman said with a broad grin as he handed David his business card.

David took his card and thanked him, and thought no more about it until he arrived at Harare airport some two weeks later.

Harare airport, although being an international airport and the main airport for the capital of Zimbabwe, was no bigger than a regional airport in the UK like Bournemouth or perhaps Leeds Bradford.

On arrival at the airport, David went into the check-in lounge. In an instant, he could see that it was packed, and all the check-in desks had at least 30-40 people queuing in front of them. The reason for it being so busy was that Zimbabwe had been hosting the All-African Games in the previous two weeks, which had ended the day that he arrived at the airport.

He looked around for someone in an official uniform. Seeing a lady, he left his bags at the back of one of the check-in queues and walked towards her.

"Hello, I wonder if you could help me, please. My name is David Roseman, and I was told to make myself known to Norman Donaldson when I arrived today." The lady's expression changed during David's conversation from believing that she might have to deal with a minor matter of inconvenience, to something much more important.

"Okay, just a minute. Norman is not on duty today, but I will see if he has left a note on his desk," the lady smiled as she went behind the check-in desks, through a door into an office. A few moments later, she returned with an envelope in her hand.

you say your name was David Roseman?" She asked _..tely.

"Yes" David replied.

"Okay, Mr. Roseman, where are your bags, please?" David pointed at his bags.

"Okay, lovely, Mr. Roseman, if you would give me your bags and follow me". The lady proceeded to walk passed the long queue in front of each check-in desk, to a check-in desk that was closed. She went behind the desk, turned on its light, and proceeded to ask for David's passport, and she then processed his boarding card as she tagged his bags and sent them onto the travelator.

"There you are, Mr. Roseman. You're booked in for an aisle seat, row 5, which is First Class on the 20.55 Air Nigeria flight to London Heathrow. Please accept this document wallet as a small appreciation for flying with Air Nigeria today." The lady handed David a letter document wallet which, when he opened it, had numerous pocket dividers for his passport, boarding pass, currency, and many other documents, that he might need whilst travelling. David smiled broadly and asked the lady to make sure that he thanked Norman Donaldson for his kindness and generosity in giving him the upgrade and the personal service.

Seeing that another check-in desk had opened, a number of the athletes in the adjacent queue moved over to stand behind David. However, as soon as David had checked in, the lady turned off the light over the desk and told those who had moved across to return to the other queues. This spare check-in desk was at the end of a row of similar desks, and thus on one side was a wall. As David walked back along this ever-lengthening queue of tired athletes, desperate to return to their countries of origin, his emotions at the stares he was receiving from these 6'4" pole vaulters, fit and very agile sprinters, and large rotund shot putters, were mixed with elation, a sense of unwarranted importance, and a fear as to what these athletic giants might say, or do to him.

Tom lived with his longstanding girlfriend in a house that her ex-husband had purchased for her as part of the divorce settlement. It was a five-storey townhouse within the curtilage of Chelsea Harbour.

David had arrived on Sunday evening, having taken the train from Leeds to London Kings Cross. Although by working within the town in which he lived, David did not need to use the trains regularly, he was always bemused at the constant criticism that was levied at the train network, as whenever he had chosen or needed to use it, it always ran to time, there were adequate seats, and the buffet cars were more than satisfactorily stocked.

One thing for sure that David realized on the tube journey to Chelsea Harbour, was that there might be a painful week ahead career-wise, but the accommodation, friendship, and relaxation of staying at Tom's house could not have been more appropriate.

David rang the doorbell to No. 11 Plainmoor Court and waited. The ground floor of the property housed a single garage, a spare bedroom/children's study playroom, and a shower room. The kitchen and formal dining room were on the first floor, and the main lounge was on the top floor, with large windows to the east and west elevation, affording wonderful views along the Thames. As no one occupied the ground floor, there was always a long delay until anyone opened the front door.

The door opened, and Tom greeted David with a warm grin, followed almost immediately by an all-encompassing bear hug.

"Alright there, Rosey," Tom said warmly whilst still embracing David.

David had never worked out whether it was an illustration of a public school upbringing, or the camaraderie resultant from playing a team sport that caused people like Tom to add a "y" or "ey" to everyone's surname to create their nickname. In fact, in David's case, Tom even amended his Christian name to "Davey" to ensure that he had two nicknames.

"Hi Tom, good to see you. How are you?" David smiled warmly in reply.

Tom Wickleby was a few years older than David, and it was a constant topic of banter as to exactly how much older Tom was than David. In reality, there were probably three years between the two of them, but David would always find a way of informing Tom that it was nearer six or seven years.

Tom was just over six feet tall, and in his later years, although he had continued to play veterans rugby well into his fifties, he had also continued to imbibe copious quantities of beer after his rugby matches, ensuring that the adjective portly was most appropriately utilized when describing him. Like David, he retained a full head of hair, although Tom's had turned grey many years ago, which, being more than a little vain, had somewhat frustrated Tom, as David's hair had yet to spawn a single grey hair.

Tom had, for a number of years, since parting company with Geoffrey Woodcombe's company, run his own very successful design company. He was also a well-respected speaker at design conferences and seminars that took him all across Europe, America, and parts of Asia. Prior to being with his current partner, he had been married to a Russian woman, and although that marriage had ended almost as soon as it had begun, he had managed to get some foothold in acquiring work in Russia, which, although noticeably reduced since his divorce to Lydia, still provided a decent income for him.

"Now then, Rosey, my friend, are you ready to be struck off?" Tom stated with a cheeky grin whilst laughing profusely at the thought of the banter he was going to create over the next few days, whilst teasing David over his career prospects during the time that David was staying with him.

"Well, funny you should say that Tom, but I have just filled out an application form to become an HGV driver on the ice road in Canada, just in case, so I am hedging my bets, yes!" They both smiled as they could mutually feel the warmth emitted between the two of them as soon as they were in each other's company.

They both went upstairs, where they were greeted by Emily, who stood expectantly in the kitchen. Like Tom, Emily offered David a warm smile followed by a similarly warm hug.

As it happened, Emily's children were staying this particular week. The children alternated, one week with Emily and one week with her ex-husband, both during school time and during the holiday period. Emily had three children that David had often heard of, but never actually met.

Within an hour of David's arrival, a roast Sunday dinner was being served, and everyone sat around the table in the kitchen. The banter flowed between everyone, and it was clear to David that, although Tom was not the children's father, there was a strong sense of mutual respect between Tom and Emily's children.

Before the evening was complete, Emily, who, as well as her own job, assisted Tom in the administration of his business, had dissected the various travel options for David the following morning. On reflection, the most obvious option, although it was the most expensive, was the water boat ferry.

A water ferry travelled along the Thames, starting in the west at Putney and winding itself eastwards along the Thames, alternating from north to south bank along its route, with its most easterly docking point being Woolwich Arsenal. The ferry picked up from Chelsea Harbour, and nine ports later, arrived just East of Blackfriars Bridge, which, as David knew, was at the end of Faringdon Street, that in turn, led to the bottom of Fleet Street. Thus, a thirty-one-minute ride on the water ferry would result in a seven-minute walk up to the International Dispute and Resolution Centre in lower Fleet Street.

David could not work out whether it was just the personality of Emily to wish to organize others, as much as she kindly did, or whether her mother hen instinct had arisen from having four children, her own three biologically, and Tom as a surrogate!

Monday, November 6th, 2017, was a bright, crisp day, and if the weather had been similar seven months earlier, one would have called it a bright Spring morning. David said goodbye to Emily and Tom, who wished him well and walked across the complex that was Chelsea Harbour. There were clearly some very prestigious apartments and houses within the complex, as well as a large hotel, that formed the focal point of part of the complex. To the rear of the hotel was a small shopping area. The shops were all independent, and irrespective of whether they were fashion shops, or antique, or art and artisan shops, pervaded a high degree of opulence.

Arriving at the gangway to the ferry, David was aware of people in front of him going into a small booth and then returning to the queue. One thing Emily had not told him was where and how to purchase a ticket. Assuming, due to the number of people going into the booth, that that was where one could purchase tickets, and not on the ferry itself, David walked to the side of the gangway and into the booth.

In front of him was a payment machine, which for the locals, was understandable and easily operational. However, for someone new to this particular system, as seemed to be the case, each and every time that someone wished to purchase a ticket from any similar machine dispenser, none of the controls seemed generic across what was ostensibly the same system. David had always wondered why, when the same criteria for purchasing a ticket existed, irrespective of the mode of transport, there was not a relatively common layout to the machine. Each machine, whether for a train, a boat, or a cinema, facilitated the same thing, the production of a ticket, based on the provision of some financial medium, following, where necessary, input as to where the ticket purchaser was going, whether it be on a train, a boat, or even to which screen in the cinema. Thus, why, when the options were so similar and so limited, did each new machine that one came across, present such an intense Mensa-like challenge, purely just to produce a ticket?

Not wishing to embarrass himself or to waste the time of others behind him, David deferred to the person entering the booth directly behind him. Having watched exactly how they had purchased their ticket, he replicated their actions and then returned to join the queue for the ferry, ticket in hand.

A few minutes later, a very sleek-looking ferry, with a glass roof appeared from upriver. David watched as the pilot overshot the gangway by twenty yards and, in doing so, immediately put the engine into reverse, so as to gently return to the jetty and allow the port side of the boat towards the stern to gently caress the edge of the jetty, in such a skillful manner as to appear to the casual observer, one of the easiest manoeuvres to undertake on the water.

A female conductor who had been waiting at the stern then quickly threw a rope over the bollard on the quayside and opened the security rail to allow passengers to get on. Immediately adjacent to the entry point, there was a digital display informing those looking to get on board, how many passengers could embark before capacity was reached. "42" was displayed in white letters on a red background. David quickly scanned the people in front of him and counted approximately sixteen ahead of him. He would be able to board this one, then he thought.

The cabin was ostensibly one large space with big cinema-like black leather seats. The roof and the sides of the ferry, down to just above seat height, were glass, allowing a panoramic view of everything that the ferry passed on its journey toward the City. In the centre of the space was a double-sided bar and coffee dispensing area. A cursory glance led David to believe that the ferry could carry about 400 passengers.

David found a forward-facing seat on the aisle of the central section of seating. As soon as the ferry moved off, he totally forgot about any mental preparation for the upcoming hearing, as he was transfixed by the splendour of the views along his journey. Clearly, at this time of day, everyone else was commuting to work and having done it numerous times before, were firmly embedded in a book, laptop, newspaper, or texting on their mobile phones, having experienced these views numerous times in the past.

Although David had lived in London for a number of years, when he was an architect, and knew London particularly well as a consequence, the only time he had been on a boat on the Thames was on an evening, on one or two of the boats that were constantly moored on The Embankment, just East of the Houses of Parliament, to meet friends for a drink. He had never taken a boat trip down the Thames. Thus, even though many of the buildings that he passed, he knew very well the perspective from which he was observing the same buildings from the river, added to his library of knowledge of the buildings and the environment in which they were set.

The atmosphere on the ferry was very calm and relaxed. A few people who were clearly couples on their way to work were chatting, but most were calmly preparing for their workday. The ferry interior was particularly clean and smacked of something run by a private company. The one-way trip from Chelsea Harbour to Blackfriars was £8.00, considerably more expensive for ostensibly the same trip on the Tube or in a bus. But the manner by which one's day unfolded emotionally was very much worth that extra cash. People on the Ferry smiled at each other and allowed others to pass by them without any sense of aggression. The whole experience was totally encompassing.

The route took David passed the refurbishment of Battersea Power Station, which was a structure, the scale of which was almost inconceivable when seen time and time again. There had been so many false dawns regarding the development of the defunct power station, the first of which commenced in the mid-1980s. However, it is believed that the current project would finally complete within the next three years.

Vauxhall Bridge, followed by Lambeth Palace on the south side of the river, the London residence of the Archbishop of Canterbury, The Houses of Parliament, The Royal Festival Hall and the rest of the South Bank and then Blackfriars Bridge, and a glimpse of Millennium Bridge, as the Ferry pulled into the jetty at Blackfriars.

David left the ferry the calmest he could have wished to have been. His only minor concern was that his mind was focused on the wonderful images that he had just experienced on the Ferry, as well the overall experience of the journey, more than he was focused on the events due to unfold today, Monday 6th November 2017.

As he considered the date, walking along Faringdon Street, he was struck by the sick co-incidence of the date. November 6th, 2008, was the date that his father was killed in a house fire. The most tragic thing about it was where his father's body had been found. It indicated that having woken up to a smoked filled house, he had come downstairs, walked past the front door, which would have taken him to safety, and instead gone to the Lounge where the open fire would have been the cause of the fire, opened the door, ostensibly to see if he could extinguish it. But the action of opening the door, not only badly burnt his hand on the metal doorknob, but also introduced oxygen to a room that the fire had depleted, resulting in a flashback that overwhelmed him and, with his heart condition, sent him into cardiac arrest, causing him to collapse and become asphyxiated by the acrid smoke.

The manner by which his father had deliberately walked past the point of safety epitomized his father's character to David. He knew that, in those moments, he would have been more livid with what he would have seen as his stupidity, in leaving the fire in a state to have caused the blaze, that his intent would have been to try and put the fire out, so that no-one would have become aware of his oversight. The fact that the fire had taken such a strong hold that anyone would have understood what had happened, even if he had been able to put it out, he did not compute. At the time, he was driven by his disgust for his own ineptitude, as he would have seen it. Such bloody-mindedness resulted in his final decision being the decision that caused his death. Such bloody-mindedness was a family trait, though, as David had realized to his cost, on many an occasion.

David had to focus on the day ahead. He was now less than 200 metres from the International Resolution and Dispute Centre, and he had still to click into gear for what could be a critical day for the future of his career.

As had occurred when he attended his Fitness to Practice Hearing some twelve months earlier, David made himself known to the Receptionist. She provided him with a name badge that read "Dr. David Roseman – Defendant." He spent a moment attaching the badge to his lower lapel as he waited for the lift to take him to the third floor, the same floor that they had used for the previous hearing.

Throughout the last three weeks, prior to the Hearing date, the interactions and communications between David, Josephine, and Malcolm had naturally become more intensive. Legal people always seemed to need a deadline before they even consider performing, let alone actually addressing matters with fervour or intent.

For a considerable period of time, David had requested Josephine ensure that she obtained documentation from the Police, that he knew would severely discredit Jenny Dolton.

Following the farcical telephone incident when Jenny had stated that her husband was going to have David done in and then refused to talk to the Police until after her golf lesson, the resultant police visit to David's clinic had to be on record. David had been demanding for weeks that this evidence, which would substantiate most of what he was saying, and further undermine what Jenny Dolton was saying, had to be produced. Both Josephine Barriston and Malcolm Finsbury had seemed more than a little apathetic to diligently acquiring this evidence. Every time that David asked if they had obtained feedback from the Police, Josephine's responses had, at best, been somewhat unequivocal. She had persistently stated that they were "on with it," but nothing then transpired materially.

It was not until ten days before the due date of the Hearing that David had laid down an ultimatum, that unless the Police evidence was produced, he would not attend the Hearing, did any action get affected.

On Thursday, 3rd November, just three days before the Hearing, Josephine confirmed that they had received a comprehensive report from the Police. She had forwarded it to Malcolm Finsbury, who had rung her back to state that "This is gold dust. This totally changes the complexion of the whole Hearing!"

In that instant, David had realized that irrespective of the status by which certain professionals project themselves, their plush offices, their hierarchical demeanour, or their exorbitant fee scales, they still are the servants of the client. They still require to be held to account, and no decision taken by them should be taken as understood, without due scrutiny.

Had it not been for the dogged persistence of David to demand that his legal team acquire the Police document, or his threat not to attend, then his fate may have been very different.

Consequent to the unearthing of the paperwork from the Police, Josephine forwarded it to the CBUK, directly after receiving Malcolm Finsbury's direction so to do.

On Saturday, 4th November, David received emails from both Malcolm and Josephine. As soon as they arrived in his email in-tray, David's initial response was to be amazed that his legal team would be working over the weekend. On reflection, he could not work out whether it was the late discovery from the Police that had caused this last-minute activity, or whether acting last minute was just how legal teams worked. Either way, at last, they seemed to be getting into gear.

Both emails from Malcolm and Josephine were ostensibly the same. Josephine had forwarded a response received from the CBUK's prosecuting barrister, that she had also received earlier, on the morning of Saturday, 3rd November.

"Following receipt of conclusive documentary evidence from the Police, in relation to the accusations tabled against Dr. David Roseman, it is now our opinion that Patient A, the complainant, is an unreliable witness. As such, we write to notify you that we will not be requesting Patient A to make a statement, or to be present at the Hearing commencing on Monday, 6th November 2017."

Although David was mildly ecstatic to read that Jenny Dolton had been deemed to be an unreliable witness, he could not understand, therefore, why the CBUK had not gone on to say that, as their only witness was deemed, by them, to be a liar, and therefore that all accusations of Unprofessional Misconduct were naturally deemed to be unreliable, that they had not stated that the case had failed and that there was consequently nothing to defend, and thus no case to answer.

During the late morning on that Saturday, David put those very points to Malcolm Finsbury. Malcolm responded, stating that, in principle, he totally agreed with David. If this had been a criminal case and the prime, let alone the sole witness, had been proven to have given false evidence before a trial, or even during a trial, the trial would have collapsed, and no further action would have been taken.

The difference in this case, according to Malcolm, was that there was a code of conduct, by which all professionals were duty-bound to practice, pertinent to their particular profession. Thus, although the complainant, as an entity, had been proven to be a liar, if certain actions, which may or may not have been admitted by the defendant, had been deemed to have been in breach of their code of conduct, then a finding of malpractice, or unprofessional conduct could still be proven. As David had, ironically following directions from his legal team, admitted to certain activities, these activities may well still be adequate to find him guilty of misconduct. The most frustrating thing that could arise is that, in order to appear to have shown a sense of vulnerability and professional conscience, his legal team had strongly suggested that he admit to certain activities, that he actually did not undertake. Had David stuck to his guns and not admitted to faults that had not actually occurred, but had done so just to appear to have undertaken due reflection and thus illustrated an attitude of contrition towards the events that had occurred, it is not inconceivable that the CBUK would have concluded, even at this late stage, that there was actually no case to answer.

Of course, the Catch-22 was that any attempt to retract what had been false admissions, and hence to honestly reflect what had actually occurred, could and most probably would have directed the CBUK to the perception that, if David was amending his statements at this late stage, and to such an extent, even though in doing so he was being more honest, (something that they would necessarily not be aware of), the CBUK might question the validity of any, or all of the other statements that he had presented to them in his previous submissions.

David once again reflected on being led along a path by the directions of his legal team, with which he had not felt comfortable, but had been persuaded to do so, based on their experience of what was deemed the correct thing to do in such circumstances.

Either way, the bottom line, following the quick-fire emails of that Saturday morning, was that everyone was to convene at the International Dispute and Resolution Centre in lower Fleet Street at 8.30.a.m. on Monday 6th November.

Arriving on the Fourth Floor, David realized that one of the minor benefits of the Fitness to Practice Hearing he had to attend twelve months before, was that he was familiar with the layout of the floor and the whereabouts of all the amenities, etc.

As was his want, David had ensured that he arrived earlier than either Malcolm or Josephine. In the corridor outside the suite of meeting rooms was a coffee-making machine and an array of various coffee options. As with the ticket dispenser at the Ferry station, it always made David smile how difficult manufacturers could make the procedure to produce something as simple as hot water added to either a tea or a coffee.

He studied the machine and, in the end, chose a bottle of water, of which there were seven different types in the cabinet beside the coffee machine. Although coffee may have been pleasant, David had noticed in recent years that, perhaps due to the caffeine in coffee, he only needed two small cups to ensure that his frequency of visiting the bathroom escalated exponentially. As it was that he was somewhat nervous anyway, he did not feel that he needed to increase the probable number of bathroom visits during the day, by adding caffeine to his system. He had regularly recalled a physiology lecture at chiropractic college, given by Andrew Clark, entitled "Two and a Half Pints," which educated the student as to the effect of alcohol, well ethanol actually, on the bladder and why the frequency of going to the toilet increased the more you went to the toilet, after drinking alcohol, although the volume one had drunk often diminished.

Both Josephine and Malcolm walked out of the lift together, having taken the 5.45 a.m. train from Manchester Piccadilly to London Euston. They had used the journey to coalesce their thoughts about how they would approach the day. Clearly, up until the previous Thursday, Malcolm had been assiduously reading and re-reading the five witness statements that Jenny Dolton had submitted to the CBUK. He had made copious notes and had been licking his lips at the possibility of tearing Dolton apart on the witness stand. There were so many contradictions within each of her statements, such that when he compared the five statements, it was difficult to construct an honest commentary as to what she was stating did actually happen.

David had been concerned, right from the start that the CBUK were attempting to stitch him up. Their protocol stated that the defendant responded to the initial complainant's witness statement; then the complainant had the option to respond to the defendant's initial response, and then the defendant had the final response, which then went to the Investigating Committee who decided if there was a case to answer. That protocol was defined within the 1994 Chiropractic Act, which, being an act of Parliament, should be adhered to, to the letter of the law. Thus, the CBUK allowing Dolton four responses to David's responses was in breach of the law. When David had mentioned this to Josephine Barriston, she had said that the more statements Dolton was allowed to make, the more the probability that she would undermine her position. As it happened, that is exactly what occurred, but because Dolton was not now going to be taking the stand, the jewels that she had presented to the defense team could not now be exploited.

As on the previous occasion, David and his legal team had been allocated a small room at the end of the corridor. Due to the subdivision of the spaces on each floor, this room was pentagonal in shape. It was not possible for three people to sit on opposite sides of the small conference table, as one edge was too close to the wall. Nor was it possible for three people to sit around the table without one getting up, should any of the others wish to exit the room, as opening the door would be fouled by the chair of the person sitting at the table. Cosy would be a polite adjective to describe the room, which would be the hub of discussions for possibly the next week.

Due to Dolton being deemed to be an unreliable witness and thus not going to take the stand, Malcolm stated that the duration of the Hearing would be noticeably reduced. But he still felt it might last the week.

Once Malcolm and Josephine had acquitted themselves with both a coffee and some biscuits, all three of them sat around the conference table.

"So, first, to let you know, David, that nothing will move swiftly during this Hearing. In fact, most of the time, you will not believe that it is possible to move so slowly. Now I have picked up on your personality, and I know that being here in the first place frustrates the hell out of you, let alone the manner by which the process winds along. So please ensure that you keep your calm at all times. We have mentioned you taking the stand. Most often, I feel that it does not add to your defense, but at all times, that is your right and prerogative to take the stand, and if you should wish to do so, then that will be fine."

"Okay, thanks, Malcolm. Well, obviously, I wi'
the knowledge and experience you have in deal
matters before, but I will inform you if I feel it is ⸜
some type of statement." David stated calmly but assertively.

"So, what happens throughout today?" David asked.

"Well, first, I make myself known to the other barrister, and we discuss any variations to the initial complaint. Then the Hearing will be convened so that all the protagonists get introduced, and any additional papers can be presented to the Panel. The panel will then adjourn, and read all the documentation, and then, when they are up to speed, we will reconvene, and the prosecution will make its case to the Panel." Malcolm outlined.

"So, you mean that the panel will not have read all the papers leading up to this yet? How bizarre is that? What a waste of time that they did not have to read the back story before arriving here!"

"Yep, well, I know, but that is the system, and it is that sort of thing that will frustrate you. But it is precisely that sort of thing that you cannot allow to get under your skin." Malcolm smiled warmly towards David.

Half an hour passed with little conversation. It is not easy to maintain considered silence, in a small room with two people one hardly knows, whilst contemplating the prospects of one's future that would be decided in the next few days.

The silence was broken by a knock on the door. The court usher looked around the door. David was unsure if that was all she would do in such a situation, or if she had realized that it would be impossible to enter the room with everyone sitting around the table.

"Mr. Finsbury, the prosecuting barrister, would like to meet with you, please." the Usher said in a clear but soft voice. The Usher was a woman in her mid-forties, of slim, well-groomed appearance, who was wearing the quintessential outfit, one saw in all legal offices and courtroom dramas and documentaries; a fitted pencil pinstriped skirt, with a cream blouse on top. Her make-up was somewhat understated, and her lipstick of a pastel tone.

Malcolm stood up, put on his suit jacket, which, again, to conform to the legal profession, was charcoal grey, with a white shirt and a navy blue tie, and picked up his notepad.

"See you shortly," he said as he exited the room.

Felicity Musselbrough was a barrister who had been instructed by the CBUK on a number of occasions previously. She was a tall, elegant, slim blonde-haired woman in her mid to late forties. She was known in legal circles to be tenacious, but fair. She would do all she could to optimize the case that she had before her, but she was a barrister who saw her job as a method to pay for her children to attend private school, and to afford herself three fortnightly holidays per year, with a few weekend breaks thrown in between. She was a woman who enjoyed going to live theatre and had a passion for Shakespeare.

Felicity had never met Malcolm, as this was the first time that he had been instructed by a legal team dealing with CBUK cases. Bellman's and Josephine Barriston, in particular, had yet to lose a CBUK case, and thus, due to the potential pitfalls in this case, it was felt necessary to instruct a hard-hitting barrister, who, if necessary, was extremely ruthless in battening down on the pertinent and significant points, as well as being very cutting when it came to cross-examinations.

Felicity Musselbrough offered an outstretched arm toward Malcolm Finsbury.

"Felicity Musselbrough, nice to meet you," Felicity said with a warm smile.

"Malcolm Finsbury, a pleasure to meet you too," Malcolm responded with similar cordiality.

"Well, a few things have changed in recent days," Malcolm stated with raised eyebrows.

"Indeed they have," Felicity responded.

"If I am honest with you, after the events of last week, the surfacing of the documentation from the Police, and the resultant decision of the CBUK to categorise Dolton as an unreliable witness, I am surprised that the case was not dropped," Malcolm stated in a fashion that clearly showed that he was fishing to attempt to ascertain Felicity's drive for a decision of guilty.

"Well, I know what you mean, Malcolm, and from the nature of your question, I sense that in your previous post, your advice as chief prosecutor for the General Medical Council would have been to drop the case," Felicity responded, again, in a fashion similar to Malcolm's fishing to his approach to such matters.

"Mmm, well, as we both know, every case is assessed on its merits, but from all the contradictions that I read from the complainant, I think I may well have directed the GMC to withdraw the case, yes." Malcolm's tone was assertive, but he wanted to ensure that he did not appear to suggest to Felicity, whose Curriculum Vitae informed him that she had much less experience in similar cases than him, that she had not advised the CBUK correctly. Of course, he did not know who had actually been involved in the decision process throughout the case. His belief, from his previous experience, and the information he had received from Josephine, was that the manner by which the CBUK undertook disciplinary matters was far less well-defined, considered, and coordinated than the GMC. Now, part of the reason for this may well have been due to the short history of the existence of the CBUK relative to the GMC. Also, the GMC governed over 40,000 GPs and hospital doctors and was funded commensurate with the requisite subscriptions attained from that many practitioners. The CBUK, on the other hand, governed 3,500 chiropractors, and even though the validity of their governance had to be to the same level of integrity as the GMC, the mere fact that the CBUK, by the fact that their income stream was considerably less than the GMC, meant that they could not employ the same level of legal expertise as the GMC, caused the wheels of its administrative system to be less well oiled, than was possible at the GMC.

"Well, I think that, when the Investigating Committee looked at a number of the issues involved in this case, they believed that there were a number of misdemeanours that could, irrespective of the validity of the witnesses' statements, constitute a case for unprofessional misconduct," Felicity said, realizing that she might be getting drawn into the depth of conversation that she did not believe might be advisable, particularly at this stage of the proceedings.

"It is imperative that I tell you that Ms. Dolton/ Mrs. Rossington turned up this morning at the time that we had requested her to arrive, when we informed her of the date of the Hearing, some six weeks ago. We appreciate what occurred on Thursday last week, but despite the decision we undertook then, we wished to confront her with the information that had been obtained from the Police, face to face," Felicity started to explain to Malcolm.

"Well, I can well understand that stance, yes," Malcolm responded.

"So, she arrived just before 10.00 a.m. this morning, and I took her into an anteroom. I informed her that I had received details from the Police, in regard to certain activities that they had been involved in. I informed her that the Police's commentary came from an independent and unbiased position and thus held a great degree of validity, particularly in a "he said, she said" scenario that occurs in a private treatment room. She listened intently and without any sense of expressive concern that I could easily elicit from her demeanour. I went on to inform her that when we assimilated the Police evidence, with the evidence and statements that she had submitted, and within the auspices of being true and honest records, we had no option other than to conclude that a degree of what she had stated was untruthful, and thus, as it was not possible to ascertain, what was truthful and what was not, based on the fact that she had said that it all was truthful, we had no other option than to define her as an unreliable witness, and as such, to be unable to use her as a witness." Felicity explained.

"And what did she say?" Malcolm asked.

"She seemed non-plussed, as if she knew that she had spoken a pack of lies and was not at all surprised to have been found out. I wonder whether she was actually surprised that it had taken until the eleventh hour, for her to be found out in such a manner," Felicity added.

"So, was she at all contrite or apologetic?" Malcolm questioned.

"No, not at all. She offered no explanation, no apology, mostly because she sensed that any explanation that she could offer would be tainted, with an attempt to regain some credibility, and she had created such a big hole full of lies to attempt to justify her action, would only bury her deeper into the mire. However, after a short pause and silence, she asked what had happened now. I informed her that she was not needed and therefore was free to go home." Felicity completed with a rueful smile.

"Was her husband with her?' Malcolm asked. "As I understand, from speaking with Dr. Roseman, that he is a very aggressive, vindictive, and vexatious man. From what he has said of some of the stories that have involved the husband, I sense that he is a very difficult man and probably the driving force behind the whole of this matter. It would seem surprising if he did not attend. I am also slightly surprised that he did not wish to make a witness statement and perhaps insinuate how much Dr. Roseman's actions had affected him emotionally." Malcolm said questionably.

"Well, it's funny that you should say that because during the investigation process, I understand that Ms. Dolton was very cautious about when and how the investigating committee contacted her. She stated that her husband was an aggressive, violent, and angry man, who could fly off the handle at any point when the matter was raised." Felicity said.

"It all appears very odd to me if I am honest. It seems that nothing actually happened physically, and definitely nothing sexually, and it would appear that she is not really that bothered about the complaint, and maybe would have even withdrawn it, or not even raised it in the first place, had it not been for the oppressive attitude of her husband." Malcolm espoused.

"I believe that is the long and the short of it, Malcolm. I believe that we would not be here at all, and Dr. Roseman would not be looking at his career being suspended on a knife edge if it was not for the one-sided nature of Ms. Dolton's relationship with her husband. I am not sure, if I am honest, in the real scope of life, if David Roseman has done anything untoward other than offer some solace and comfort to a scared and frightened woman. Sadly, though, in expressing his altruism, he may well have fallen foul of the strict letter of the Chiropractic Code of Conduct, particularly the manner by which the activity of a "sexual act" is defined." Felicity said in a conciliatory tone.

"Yes, when you think of a single male, working alone in a clinic, where he treats a woman, who by definition, may often be in a state of undress, he is constantly at the risk of the sanity of the patients he is treating. Also, as a businessman attempting to increase his patient base, if he does not accept civil courtesies from patients he sees within the environs of his clinic, for fear of being accused of accepting a date, and thus undertaking a sexual act, as defined in the Code of Conduct, he could be misconstrued as uncommunicative and unfriendly, and thus not someone that a prospective patient would wish to visit. Nightmare, a real nightmare!" Malcolm said with a degree of passion in his voice.

"I totally agree, Malcolm, I totally agree, it is not at all easy, for a male practitioner particularly. But sadly, we are here to administer the rights and wrongs, as stipulated by the letter of the law and the codes of conduct, not to appraise guilt based on our own moral judgments or personal moral codes." Felicity said in a very resigned manner.

After this interaction, Malcolm understood that the sympathies of the prosecuting barrister were definitely with his client, although due to the position she held as the prosecutor, she had to attempt to find his client guilty of unprofessional conduct. Malcolm postulated that even if the prosecution did succeed in convincing the Panel of David's guilt, there was not a stomach for any serious sanction, if anything, more than an admonishment.

Malcolm returned to the meeting room, somewhat emboldened by his conversation with Felicity. Although he believed, at this early stage, that the outcome might be a little more positive for David than he had perceived, when he read the papers initially, some six weeks ago, he decided not to show any sense of hope to David, beyond the reasoned positivity that any barrister should afford his client.

Chapter 13 – The Professional Conduct Hearing

Malcolm Finsbury turned the handle of the door in an attempt to enter the meeting room, to report back on his discussion with Felicity Musselbrough. Unfortunately, and somewhat comically, the handle came off in his hand, leaving only the spindle on his side of the door. The commotion that it caused alerted David, who got up and, with some dexterity, enabled the door to be opened from the inside, without the spindle and the handle internally coming off in his hand.

Malcolm entered, both bemused and somewhat amazed as to what had just happened, to find both David and Josephine attempting to hold back their laughter.

"Well, let's hope that isn't some sort of omen," Malcolm said ruefully.

"Well, in actual fact, if it is Malcolm, it could be a positive one," David replied with a beaming smile. "The last time we were here, 12 months ago, the very same thing happened, just as we were being called to go into the courtroom, and the Fitness to Practice Panel proposed no sanction to my practice during the investigation. So, who knows?" David continued.

"Do you mean that it has not been fixed for 12 months?" Malcolm said, slightly alarmed.

"Well, I am not saying that as, of course, I do not know, but with some of these cheaper handles, the screw that holds the actual handle to the spindle, the square pin that protrudes through the door and slots into the female section of the handle, is only a grub screw, secured by friction to the spindle. The better ones have a hole into which the screw fits. But where the connection is effectively by pure friction, every time one turns the handle and pulls the door closed, it affects the efficiency of the friction grip." David explained whilst gesticulating with his hands to assist his description of the fixing.

"Well, who would have thought that at a professional conduct hearing, we would learn all about the workings of door handles, Malcolm?" Josephine said with a grin.

Malcolm joined David and Josephine in laughter as they all realized how such a simple thing as a 3mm screw falling out of a hole in a door, could potentially scupper part of their day.

The door handle incident lightened the mood considerably in the meeting room as Malcolm explained his discussions with Felicity Musselbrough.

At 11.25 a.m., the clerk to the courtroom knocked on the door, and the three members of the defense team prepared themselves for the formalities to come.

The courtroom was on the other side of the building from the courtroom used at the Fitness to Practice Hearing. The room offered an easterly wall to the outside, which, at this time of day, provided some reflected sunlight into the room.

At the far end of the room, there was a long table with four high-backed chairs behind it, very similar to those at the Fitness to Practice hearing. Malcolm directed David to a desk on the right of the room, running parallel to the long table, but about two metres away from it. The table easily afforded David and Malcolm the opportunity to sit side by side. Josephine sat behind at a similar table. To the right of where David was asked to sit was a lectern-like piece of furniture, that David presumed was where anyone giving evidence would stand, as there was a copy of the Bible placed on it.

Felicity Musselbrough and her legal colleague sat at a similar desk to Malcolm and David, to the left of centre of the long desk. To the far left of the main desk was a small square table at which sat a stenographer.

Within a short period of all the prosecution and defense teams sitting down, the Court Usher called for everyone to rise. Malcolm touched David's hand to ensure that he stood up.

The three members of the panel and the legal adviser walked into the room in single file and in order of which they would sit at their seats behind the long table. A slim woman in her fifties first, who sat at the left-hand side of the desk, as viewed from David's perspective; a tall curly haired man, also in his fifties, who took the second chair, followed by a young red-haired scruffy looking man, who although wearing a shirt and tie, was clearly not used to doing so. Finally, a man in his early sixties with a receding hairline took up the fourth chair, which was positioned slightly further apart than the other three chairs. David concluded that the mid-twenty-year-old, finding it difficult to sit still, in a woolen suit that his mother had probably bought him for his eighteenth birthday party, was the chiropractor. The lady at the far end was the lay member, and the Chair was probably from the General Dental Council, or similar.

The lay member appeared to be either a mid-ranking civil servant, or a legal secretary who had retired and enjoyed the opportunity of being paid to come and visit and stay in London for a few nights in the year. The token chiropractor looked like he still required his mother to wash behind his ears and, consequently, was very unlikely to offer any comment that would be contrary to a comment made by the other two panel members. He was not going to be someone who would offer a different considered view, even though, as a fellow chiropractor and as a male chiropractor, he was the one member of the panel to most likely comprehend the unusual circumstances in which David worked.

After it was clear that everyone was in position, the Chair requested that everyone be seated. The Chair had a soft but commanding voice, which immediately gave the impression of a man who considered things before making a remark and had the mentality to carry a number of variable options in his mind at any one time.

The Chair opened his notepad and, after acknowledging that his fellow panel members were ready to proceed, looked towards Felicity Musselbrough to commence proceedings for the prosecution.

Felicity took fifteen minutes to outline all the various misdemeanours that, according to the CBUK, David had undertaken. She referenced each of the eleven accusations that Jenny Dolton had cited in her witness statements in a manner that, despite knowing that Dolton had lied, was intended to make the panel believe them, in a way as if each one was a true statement of fact.

Malcolm had warned David, prior to going into the courtroom, not to be offended by the tone of the prosecuting barrister and to definitely not react to any of the adjectives that she used, that were all designed to paint him in a bad light.

"If I am honest, David, one of the worst bits of this whole hearing will be the first twenty minutes, where the prosecuting barrister will, at best, depict you as an unprofessional misfit or, at worst, as some depraved and deprived sexual deviant, who should never be allowed to work as a chiropractor again. But do not worry. That is her job to paint the worst picture first. In doing so, she defines the parameters of her scope of work, not only to the panel but also to her paymasters, who will be reviewing her performance. What you may not realise, for obvious reasons, because you are here to fight for your career, is that the prosecutors are also, to a much lesser extent, fighting for their reputations and maybe their careers too. So, the barrister will be performing, as will I, and crudely put, using you as the subject of our performance." Malcolm smiled, knowing that the concept that others in the room were effectively using him to further their careers, was most probably the last thing that had crossed David's mind.

"Well, all I can hope, Malcolm, is that your performance is closer to Shakespeare than to Gilbert and Sullivan." David smiled ruefully and poignantly at Malcolm.

At the conclusion of her opening address Felicity looked towards Malcolm as she sat down, offering the stage to him and ending with the final remarks, "…and for that reason, members of the panel, I would ask you to find the defendant David Roseman, guilty of Serious Unprofessional Misconduct."

The hearing of that last phrase made David wince slightly. To use the term "serious" unprofessional misconduct, caused one to believe that, it was a grade above mere "unprofessional misconduct," and as such, any member of the public, hearing the term "serious" would think a greater misdemeanour had occurred than might have been the case otherwise. But in fact, in the CBUK Code of Conduct, there was only Serious Unprofessional Misconduct; there was no lower level of unprofessional misconduct, which seemed somewhat obtuse to David.

Malcolm Finsbury took a few seconds to apparently compose himself, but David knew from his own experience of performing in amateur dramatic plays that silence, pause, and expectation, are very powerful mediums to focus the attention of the audience on the upcoming protagonist.

"Mr. Chairman, members of the panel, my learned colleague, has painted a picture that she would like you to see in only one way. She would like you to see Dr. Roseman as an overpowering, scheming predator, who groomed and manipulated, a very vulnerable woman in such a way that she did things that, without his forceful predatory nature, combined with her psychological insecurities, she would not have been drawn into. The prosecution would like you to believe that

210

Patient A was a mere pawn in Dr. Roseman's game. But members of the panel, this was a 52-year-old woman. A woman who had been married and divorced and had two daughters in their twenties. A woman who worked in an occupation where she treated patients, and thus was very conversant of the line between patient and clinician; yet apparently, at no stage, in her eight treatments from the end of May to mid-June 2016, did she not realise that the boundaries were being blurred. Patient A was an attractive woman, from what we are led to believe, who we are also led to believe, had never, in her almost thirty-year career as an Occupational Therapist, come across embarrassing situations, one-to-one with patients. This was a lady who visited patients in their homes, as well as in hospitals, who, therefore, was constantly engaging in situations that might be compromising. Yet, Patient A was so naïve as not to comprehend the events that were unfolding during her frequent visits to my client's clinic. It will be our contention that although the actions of Dr. Roseman may have been somewhat beyond the perceived scope of the code of conduct under which, as a chiropractor, he practiced, many of his actions and reactions were consequential to the predatory nature of Patient A, who as a clinician herself, knew all too well, where the professional boundaries lay, and deliberately overstepped them, either for her own gratification, or because, as a woman, she saw the vulnerability of Dr. Roseman, and used him to her psychological advantage." Malcolm paused to ensure that the effect of his comments had been readily understood by the members of the panel.

"Our evidence will show that the areas where Dr. Roseman could be accused of overstepping the boundaries, only occurred in an altruistic, caring manner. You will be aware, members of the panel, that Patient A will not be presenting evidence or available for cross-examination during this Hearing. I know you will understand that in the manner by which our judicial system is set up, it is a usual, necessary prerequisite of the defense, to be able to cross-examine the prosecution witnesses. It becomes even more paramount when, due to the nature of the professional interaction, in a chiropractic clinic, there can only be one witness for the prosecution and one for the defense. Thus, I would like it to be understood that the credibility of Patient A has been clearly illustrated by the fact that the prosecution has deemed her to be an unreliable witness, and thus every point raised by the prosecution, that relies on its derivation from Patient A, has to be dismissed, as, at best conjecture, and hearsay at worst, as the lies that the action of choosing not to call the only witness and the only complainant in this case illustrate. For these reasons alone, members of the panel, I would direct you to find my client, Dr. David Roseman, not guilty of serious unprofessional misconduct." Malcolm calmly closed his small red file and sat down on his seat.

The mention of "hearsay" caused David to reflect on the situation in relation to witnesses and witness statements. At the time of the investigations, following the decision of the investigating committee that there was a case to answer, both sides could submit statements from those they believed would assist, support, or substantiate their argument. For David's defense, there were three people who had submitted statements that supported his argument. Gordon Fenton, David's friend from the Bulls Head, Tim Compton, who had been with David the night that they observed the Rossington's at The Bull and Baby pub, and Wendy Wordsley, who was the lady who did David's bookkeeping.

In looking to prepare his defense, David had been told by Josephine, that all witnesses that the CBUK wished to attend to make their case would be paid for by the CBUK. However, any witnesses that David wished to attend, would have to be paid for by David personally. David had responded by saying that, as all his witnesses had provided signed witness statements, why would they need to attend the hearing at all? Josephine informed David that, due to the quirk of law, although the signed witness statements were taken as bona fide before they got to court, where there was a court situation, unless those who had written the signed statements, attended court, then their evidence was deemed to be "hearsay," and hearsay had a lower level of credibility than the exact same content, within the signed statement being read out in open court.

Feeling somewhat aggrieved at those two facts, David had contacted his chiropractic association to see if his insurance covered the costs of loss of income, travel expenses, and overnight accommodation costs for any witnesses. He believed that, as the insurers were covering the legal costs, and thus defense costs, the appearance of witnesses, must fall into the categorization of defense costs.

Following questioning of the ECA, who were the professional conduit to the insurers, David was informed that the costs incurred by the loss of income and travel expenses of his prospective witnesses would not be covered.

Although he could not categorically be assured of the reasons why the insurers would not carry such a cost, David wondered whether the President of the English Chiropractic Association, Charles Taylor, might have used his influence in the matter.

The President of the English Chiropractic Association was a diminutive man, both in stature and in character and personality, called Charles Taylor. A few weeks after David had received notification of the complaint against him, and consequently the exact same time frame after he had notified the ECA, he attended an Extraordinary General Meeting of the ECA, which was held at the time of one of their bi-annual conferences.

Chiropractors, like most other professionals, were duty-bound by the terms and conditions of their registration to undertake a certain amount of continued professional development (CPD), throughout the year, ostensibly to ensure that they kept up to date with the current trends in their profession. In total, each professional had to complete thirty hours per year on CPD. The composition of those hours could vary from reading, engaging with other chiropractors within their own clinics to discuss particular cases, etc., or attending a conference. Attending a conference would entitle them to just over twenty-five percent of their annual CPD hours for the year. Thus, the sole reason most associations facilitated conferences was to provide their members with these hours of CPD. Clearly, for many members, the content of the lectures and seminars never improved the chiropractor's knowledge base, but it did facilitate the opportunity of meeting colleagues and old college friends, at the same time as acquiring the necessary CPD hours towards their annual quota.

The reason for the extraordinary general meeting was because there were many members who believed that the actions of Charles Taylor were not as laudable as he would have the members believe. Indeed, there was strong evidence that he had an agenda to radically alter the structure and ethos of the longest-established chiropractic organization in the country.

During the meeting, the devious nature of Charles Taylor was illustrated by Ian Mackintosh, who, although having lived and practiced in Sheffield for 30 years, was as strong a diehard Scot as it was possible to meet. There was no messing with Ian. He said it as it was and had no compunction about causing offence, with either his delivery or the content of his commentary. Ian had played rugby back in his day, and he was of the stature to be a perfect No.8. When at school, after a short training session, the rugby master decided that there would be twenty minutes of a game to conclude the session, you would always want to be wearing the same shirt as Ian Mackintosh.

David had found an affinity with Ian, and although he was not that cognizant of the specifics of the quarrel within the ECA, would happily hang his flag on Ian's mast before considering supporting Charles Taylor.

The resultant of the extraordinary meeting was that there would be a review of certain matters, and a report submitted to members, prior to there being another extraordinary general meeting to hopefully provide clear directions for the future of the ECA.

Like Ian Mackintosh, David had been very vocal at the EGM, and his dissension towards the opinion of the President had been duly noted by those sitting on the Top Table, at the meeting.

The Monday following the EGM, David contacted the Chief Executive of the ECA and requested a copy of the Constitution. Before he put pen to paper and made any proposals, David had wished to be knowledgeable as to the content of the Constitution, so that he was conscious of the scope of possibilities that were available.

The day after he had requested a copy of the Constitution, the phone rang in the clinic reception of Silkmoor Chiropractic Clinic.

"Good afternoon, Silkmoor Chiropractic Clinic," David said in his clear dulcet tones.

"Good afternoon, may I speak with David Roseman, please?" a weak-sounding, relatively high-pitched voice, for an adult male at least, replied.

"Yes, its David speaking, whose calling, please?" David responded, recognizing the voice instantly.

"It's Charles Taylor, President of the ECA." Taylor replied.

"Oh, hello, Charles," responded David, smiling to himself as he did. "How can I help you?"

"Ah, well," Taylor responded somewhat gingerly. "Well, I understand that you have requested a copy of the Constitution?" Taylor continued.

Hearing the uncertainty in Taylor's voice, David knew that he would enjoy playing Taylor along in the next few minutes. "Yes, that's right," David said, deliberately not offering anything other than the least necessary answer to the question.

"Oh, ok, well, I, umm, was just wondering if anything was wrong?" Taylor responded.

Beginning to enjoy the predicament now, David asked, "Sorry, in what way, Charles?"

"Well... I wondered.... if there was anything that you were,..... were concerned about, or anything that I could,... that I could, could help you with?" Taylor replied in a very unimpressive and fumbling manner.

"Oh, I see, well that is very kind of you to offer, Charles, and similarly in taking the time to call me, but no, no, there is nothing that I think you can help me with. But now that you have been kind enough to call, I will definitely get back to you, if I think of anything." David replied, beaming from ear to ear at the way Taylor was fumbling and fishing for information.

"Oh, okay, well, yes, well, okay, well, yes, if there is anything that I can help you with, then please let me know," Taylor said, again clearly frustrated that David had not provided him with any incite, as to why David had asked for a copy of the Constitution, directly following the EGM, the weekend before.

"That's very kind, thanks again for ringing Charles, take care, bye-bye." David put the phone down and just sat for a few minutes, cogitating what had just happened.

The President of his association, an association of 80% of the chiropractors within the UK, had just contacted him, ostensibly to try and find out whether David was hatching anything to undermine his position as president. How more devious, or self-serving could Taylor have illustrated himself to have been?

The nature of Taylor's real character dawned on David a few moments later. The ECA had openly prided itself on claiming that it provided very intense pastoral care, for each and every chiropractor, should any assistance be needed. In a situation where a chiropractor has been notified of a complaint against them by their governing body, the ECA is deemed to have a pastoral team, consisting of experienced chiropractors who contact the accused chiropractor as soon as possible and offer their help and assistance, in any way that the accused wishes. The main protagonist of such pastoral care is the President of the Association. David had notified the ECA of his predicament two weeks before the EGM. Charles Taylor would have been fully aware of David's situation prior to the meeting. Even if, for some bizarre reason, he had not been notified, he would have been aware, as a result of the EGM, as David made specific reference to his case during his commentary at the EGM, if only in reasonably generic terms.

Thus, with all that information to hand, and being the President of the Association that was meant to provide the closest professional support to David, Charles Taylor had chosen to ring up to quiz David about what he might be doing that might affect the future, as President, of Taylor and not to adopt the pastoral role, that as President, he was duty bound to do.

"Shit, what an absolute twat," David shouted out when he had computed what had actually occurred in those previous five minutes.

*****

217

"Thank you, Mr. Finsbury," the Chair responded as Malcolm resumed his seat. "At this point, I would suggest that we break for a coffee and consider the opening statements made by the prosecution and the defense counsels." In completing his sentence, the Chair rose and, in doing so caused the rest of the courtroom to rise and watch him and the other members of the panel file out.

David looked at Malcolm in amazement. "Is it normal to adjourn as soon as we have commenced, Malcolm? At this rate, we will be here all week." David stated, somewhat frustrated.

"Well, yes, that is the norm, and I am afraid that you are going to have to get used to the fact that, in law, nothing, but nothing moves at pace. In fact, from my personal experience, I am not sure that anything in life moves at a slower pace than matters involving the law. Regrettably, it just is what it is, I'm afraid," Malcolm responded ruefully.

The three members of the defense team waited until the prosecution filed out and then walked back to their meeting room.

At 2.10 p.m., the Court Usher circulated both meeting rooms to request that each team reassemble in the courtroom. The courtesies and formalities of the entrance of the Panel once again undertaken, the Chair addressed Felicity Musslebrough and asked her to substantiate the case that she had outlined in the morning session.

"It has been accepted that due to the irrefutable evidence provided by the Police, none of the witness statements provided by Patient A can be submitted here, as it has been concluded that this witness is unreliable. However, during the course of our investigations, it has been concluded that the actions of Dr. Roseman, many of which have been admitted, in their own right, constitute actions deemed to be in contravention of the Code of Conduct set out in the 1994 Chiropractors Act, and therefore require the Panel to find Dr.

Roseman guilty of unprofessional conduct." Musselbrough paused for effect.

"The actions that constitute a breach of professional conduct are as follows:-

- Dr. Roseman provided chiropractic treatment to Patient A between 20 May and 10 June 2016;
- Between 24 May and 10 June 2016, they became friends on the social media site "Facebook," and Dr. Roseman shared photographs of Patient A on his Facebook account;
- On 15 June 2016, Dr. Roseman took Patient A to a spa, gave her a bikini and a power kite, took her to lunch, and paid for a spa treatment for her;
- On one or more dates in August and September 2016, Dr. Roseman contacted Patient A on her mobile telephone asking to meet up and saying, "can I see you?" or words to that effect, and sent her emails saying, "you are not on your own" and "I am here for you" or words to that effect;
- Between 24 May, and 9 August 2016, Dr. Roseman had lunch with Patient A at the Station Café in Silkmoor and, on one or more occasions, suggested that she work as a private occupational therapist from a room at his premises and discussed the possibility of employing her as his Practice Manager;
- On an occasion in September 2016, Dr. Roseman attended Patient A's home address;
- In September 2016, Dr. Roseman caused or allowed a friend to contact Patient A to discuss her complaint [to the CBUK] against him;

The actions cited here give a clear illustration of sexual intent by the defendant and constitute actions that cumulatively amount to a course of conduct that amounts to unacceptable professional conduct.

- The behaviour in respect of the Facebook account and the spa visit was a failure to maintain a clear professional relationship;
- The behaviour in respect of the spa visit and the mobile telephone messages in August and September 2016 was sexually motivated.

Thus, it is the supposition of the General Chiropractic Council that this Panel must find Dr. David Roseman guilty of Severe Unacceptable Unprofessional Misconduct."

Feeling like she had presented the case as succinctly but also as forcibly as she could have done, Felicity Musselbrough sat back down on her chair.

Malcolm Finsbury completed his notes following the presentation made by Felicity Musselbrough and awaited directions from the chair.

"Thank you, Ms. Musslebrough. We have now been directed to the information provided and would like to hear from Mr. Finsbury in response. However, I see that due to the time, I imagine that we will not be able to hear all of Mr. Finsbury's response before we close today and thus suggest that we adjourn until 10.00 a.m. tomorrow when we will take the submission of the Defense.

Thus, the formal part of the hearing finished just before 4.00 p.m. once again, Malcolm, David, and Josephine returned to their meeting room.

Day Two would predominantly be the day for the Defense. The day when David would either take the stand to be questioned by Malcolm and, importantly, cross-examined by Felicity Musselbrough, or choose not to subject himself to cross-examination.

Malcolm had been able to appraise Felicity during her prosecution presentation and came to the conclusion that he did not think that she had a powerful cutting edge to her, which caused him to believe that, either due to her own personality, or the personality of this case, she would not be a barrister that would wish to rip David apart, should he choose to take the stand.

"Now, the main issue we need to decide before we go home today is whether you wish to, or should take the stand tomorrow David. Obviously, there is no requirement for you to take the stand, and whether you do or don't direct the Panel, in any way, towards your guilt or, similarly, towards your innocence. Clearly, if you should choose not to take the stand, the presentation of your case is totally in our hands. Anything that the prosecuting barrister should say to counter my comments cannot be totally verified, as she would not have had the opportunity to cross-examine you. Of course, should you choose to take the stand because you believe that your describing the events might add weight to your defense, it is totally your judgment. But if you should decide to, then of course, it might only require the prosecution to trip you up on one issue, or should I say, perceive to have tripped you up, for that to have an uncertain influence on the interpretation of the truth, and thus their findings." Malcolm explained as well as his twenty-five years of experience in dealing with professional conduct cases allowed him.

"Well, there is a large part of me that is willing and, in fact, wants to take the stand, as in my opinion, it is an injustice that I am here at all, let alone, by definition, being subjected to the possibility of being found guilty. Thus, I have a sense of wanting to have my say. I am confident to be on the stand. My experience on the stage means that I don't have any stage fright, which would deter me from going on the stand. However, I will be directed by you and your experience and opinion, Malcolm." David said in a calm and considered manner.

"From where we are, the fact that she has been deemed to be unreliable, the nature of the evidence being your word against hers, I would say that currently, we are on the right side of the curve, and although the emotion of your delivery may assist the Panel in its opinion, there is a greater possibility of Felicity Musselbrough landing one blow that would undermine the benefit of the Panel hearing from your own mouth, what they have read already to be the case," Malcolm said in a manner that David readily understood, was telling him not to go on the stand.

"Okay, I will not go on the stand tomorrow, then," David said with a sigh.

"Great, fine, well I think that you have made the correct decision there. The next thing we need to discuss relates to the timeframe between you discharging her, going out to lunch with her, and her going away for the wedding." Malcolm said. "It appears to me that all things that happened, communications and meetings after they returned from the wedding, are not forming part of the Hearing here. It appears to me that it has been accepted that sufficient time had elapsed from being discharged as a patient for anything that occurred after the middle of July to be deemed not pertinent to the case."

"Yes, I would agree with that," David responded. "But as I have repeatedly told you, the meeting that happened on the Wednesday after I discharged her on the Friday before, only happened because of the impending flight to Portugal on the Saturday after and the resultant wedding. Had her wedding not been for a month after I had discharged her, I would not have felt it pertinent to meet with her so soon after discharging her. Thus, it is very important that we inform them, of the close proximity of the departure for the wedding, to the date of discharging her from my chiropractic care." David stated in a similar fashion, as he had stated at least three times during his meetings with Malcolm and Josephine leading up to the Hearing.

"If she had not been uncertain whether she was doing the right thing in marrying Rossington, then it would not have been necessary to have met with her before they left for the wedding. Wednesday was the only feasible possibility, as I had a busy clinic the other days of the week, and Wednesday was my day off. They were leaving for Manchester airport early on Saturday morning, and due to the apparent controlling nature of Rossington, the possibility of meeting one evening would have been totally unfeasible. So, time was of the essence. To be honest, my interest was in providing a reassuring shoulder to someone who was definitely in a quandary. I believed that I had serviced my professional liability by discharging her when I did. If I am honest, once I had discharged her, I was not cognizant of a pertinent time factor that professionally would have been deemed necessary as a cooling-off period. Even if I had been aware of a particular time frame that, on review of the code of conduct, I have not come across, , I probably would not have adhered to it. Once again, solely because I believed that her state of mind, and the clarity of her decision processes about a life-changing choice, was what was paramount. So, I believe we must put that fact across, which, if accepted, genuinely should dilute any concern about the lack of time spent after discharge, which, as I say again, must be open to interpretation, as no time is actually specified in the Code of Conduct." David elucidated once more. To him, he could see that the chronology and the timing were obvious. Perhaps because he was the one person who knew what his real intent had been.

It was clear that he had been flattered by the attention given to him by Jenny, and it was also clear that if he had not been so depressed and low, he would most probably not have acted in such a cavalier manner as others had thought. However, he knew the genuine nature of his actions that Wednesday lunchtime. Although he was interested in Jenny, if she had been single, he would probably have wished to have a relationship with her. But with all that said, he could also act altruistically, and at that particular moment, his greatest concern was that Jenny made the correct decision for her, over and above any concern for himself or for no one else.

David could see that, despite the passion of his explanation, and the clear genuine nature of his explanation, Malcolm was very reticent to present what were the facts to the Panel.

"The issue I have with presenting the chronology as it actually occurred, David, is this. This is a governing body assessing you as one of its registrant chiropractors, solely within the spectrum of whether you adhered to their code of conduct and whether you acted ethically within the period that Dolton was a patient at your clinic. Now there were, through your own admissions, some indicators that should have alerted you to the probability of there being issues with this woman, which should really have caused you to most probably discharge her, and refer her to another chiropractor, sooner than you did. Clearly, if you had other chiropractors in your clinic at the time, both their availability and the fact that they might have observed something could have facilitated the correct actions earlier. Then, if she had been being treated by another clinician, any social, altruistic action would have been further from the time of discharge and been deemed acceptable. But we are considering what should have been done in hindsight, which is a very unproductive thing to do. No, sadly, they are not going to be able to distinguish five days from discharge to the lunch meeting as anything other than being too close a period to disregard your professional duty of care. Of course, they may even consider that you were even more devious by deliberately discharging her so that you could inform them that you had realized an unwarranted connection, technically discharged her, so that you could appear to be compliant with the code of conduct, but had already decided to take her to lunch before you discharged her five days before." Malcolm paused as he could see David was getting somewhat frustrated as to his line of thought.

"The one thing I do not want them to surmise is that your actions were premeditated, as then, even your statement of discharging her

224

and the credibility of the date that you did discharge her becomes questionable," Malcolm stated.

"But Malcolm, the credibility of my notes has been proven via forensic evidence. The concept that the notes may have been tampered with, altered, or doctored in any way has been disproved. The beauty of those notes is that the initial part is filled in by the patient and signed accordingly. Dolton's signature was on the notes. Those notes were then filled in as pertinent, during the treatment, and the necessary notes in relation to both the treatment undertaken and the points of interest regarding her actions and comments were noted appropriately also. So, there is no questioning the timing of her discharge." David stated, seeing that despite the angle he attempted to address this argument, Malcolm was refusing to buy it.

"Listen, I think we should all call it a day now, consider everything that has been said, and both review our respective positions overnight and, when appropriate, revisit our wishes tomorrow. Because, ultimately, you are the client here, and although we are here to advice, the fundamental is that we are here to take your instructions and act upon them, according to your wishes." Malcolm said with a warm, reassuring smile.

David agreed. The three of them then packed up their files and headed out into the darkened November skies.

Despite being November, the temperature was not cold. David walked down lower Fleet Street and turned right along Faringdon Street, towards Blackfriars and the jetty to catch the Ferry back to Tom and Emily in Chelsea Harbour.

The Thames was becalmed as he waited for the Ferry. Within ten minutes, the western ferry had arrived. Finding a seat on the boat was relatively simple, and David relaxed as he contemplated the day just passed and the following day to come, as he took in the landmark sights, now under floodlights, as the ferry moved towards Chelsea.

The bar was open, so David decided to enjoy a gin and tonic and ease his way into the evening. He considered the alternative to the relaxation of the ferry, the hassle of the Tube at this time of night, and thanked his good fortune that he had kept in touch with Tom Wickleby after he moved away from London.

As is always the case, on the return journey, the trip upriver to Chelsea Harbour seemed to take half the time that the journey down to Blackfriars had taken, some nine hours before. No more than twelve people alighted the ferry at Chelsea Harbour, and David walked purposefully but relatively slowly around the marina and across the hotel frontage, before he turned into the secluded courtyard where 11 Plainmoor Court was situated.

David pressed the doorbell and waited to see who would come and let him in.

Tom opened the door and, in the same manner as the night previously, greeted his long-term friend with a warm smile, handshake, and hug.

"So, Rosey, how did it go? Clearly, they haven't decided to send you down yet, then?" Tom said, laughing heartedly as was often the case when he had said something cheeky, that he believed to also be hilarious.

David just smiled knowingly and suggested that the two of them went out for a quick beer, which they both did, before returning to Emily's delicious Lamb Henry dinner.

The trip to Blackfriars Bridge on Tuesday 7th, November was very similar to the day before. The Thames was again becalmed, the clouds were high in the sky, and as David did not need to be in Fleet

226

Street until just after 9.00 a.m., he took a later ferry and enjoyed a relaxed coffee on the boat.

As with all court routines, the protocol for the entrance of the committee unfolded as the day before.

"Mr. Finsbury, would you like to present your submissions, please?" the Chair smiled as he directed Malcolm to take centre stage.

"Members of the panel, the main issue before you relates to your perception of the intent of Dr. Roseman when considering the actions that the prosecution counsel put before you yesterday. Each of the actions outlined did occur to some degree or another. Dr. Roseman does not deny that in principle. However, the main area of debate is whether each event was undertaken as part of a whole, and thus whether each event should be seen as part of a sequential activity, or whether each event should be seen as an individual action that, just by the very fact that one followed the other, and in essence sequential, does not make them anything more than a sequence of individual events. Of course, if you believe it to be the former, then it is not necessarily the severity of each individual event that would constitute an act of unprofessional conduct, but the totality of the whole, which may cause you to believe that, collectively, unprofessional conduct had occurred. Similarly, if you felt that each event was independent, but that one alone might be grave enough to constitute unprofessional conduct, then your choice is clear." Malcolm paused for a moment to take a drink of water from the glass on the table in front of him.

"It is Dr. Roseman's contention that once he realized that Patient A had expressed emotional interest towards him, he discharged her from his clinic. The patient file that was forensically verified as being a true record clearly confirms that. Now whether you believe that Dr. Roseman should have seen signs at an earlier stage, may cause you to consider reasonable criticism of his slowness to act. However, that in itself is not grounds for finding someone guilty of unprofessional conduct. Also, as Dr. Roseman states, he was aware of the short time parameters for Patient A's condition to improve. If he had not been a sole practitioner at the time, he would have asked that one of his colleagues take over the care of Patient A. However, Dr. Roseman contests that his first aim was to care for his patient and that although he did see some early warning signs, he felt that his greatest concern was the treatment of his patient. So, is it correct to criticize a clinician who sacrifices his situation for the benefit of his patient's treatment outcome?"

"Dr. Roseman admits purchasing the gift of a bikini and a kite. He also admits entertaining Patient A to lunch some five days after discharging Patient A. Patient A states that the lunch date must have been pre-booked or premeditated, as it involved treatment at a spa hotel. If this was so, then it is possible that Dr. Roseman did deliberately discharge Patient A, with the intent of taking her out a few days later. But in fact, evidence received from Blunton Lodge Hotel clearly indicates that Dr. Roseman contacted the hotel on the morning of their visit to the hotel. Analysis of his telephone records, and the time of the booking of the spa treatment on the hotel records, illustrate that they were made at 09.40 a.m. on Wednesday, 15th June. This concurs with the time that Patient A unexpectedly arrived at his clinic. She was aware that his clinic was closed on a Wednesday but still chose to turn up. Why would a patient turn up at a clinic that was known to be closed if all she intended was to be a patient?" Malcolm took another sip of his water.

"We know, from a signed statement from Wendy Wordsley, the clinic bookkeeper, that Patient A did turn up at just after 9.00.a.m on that Wednesday. So, it seems clear that the act of all the events at Blunton Lodge Hotel was spontaneous and not part of a sequential event." Malcolm's eyes scanned the panel to see if he could gauge if they had comprehended his thought process.

"Now, the prosecution has stated that the act of taking Patient A to Blunton Lodge, that act alone, was sufficient to find guilt of unprofessional conduct. However, interestingly, events that happened a number of weeks later, like the meeting for lunch, or the walk on the Moors, which required the same level of intent, were not deemed of significance, or relevance, to be cited as inappropriate actions, even though they were admitted, to be actions that constituted being categorized as unprofessional conduct. Thus, the only issue that seems that is to be considered is whether there was adequate time from the discharging of Patient A until the going for lunch at Blunton Lodge."

"What we also have to remember is that at no stage, at no stage at all, did Patient A state that she was forced to engage in a meeting or forced to go with Dr. Roseman in his car to Blunton Lodge. Patient A, who is also a medical clinician, willingly and voluntarily went with and sometimes instigated the mutual communications and meetings with Dr. Roseman. Patient A, due to her medical background, her training, and her day-to-day interaction with patients, should not be considered as most other non-medical patients would be. It is understood that due to the existence of the "white coat syndrome," patients can be deemed to be in a subservient position to any medical clinician, and hence codes of conduct are written within the parameters of believing that most patients may be affected, in greater or lesser degrees by the "white coat syndrome." However, I would strongly suggest that Patient A, due to the fact that, not only did she work as a clinician, but more specifically, due to her actual career as an Occupational Therapist, where she interacted with patients and clinicians more senior than herself, the white coat syndrome, which the prosecution is intimating was pertinent, would not have been the case with Patient A." Malcolm stopped to take a sip of water from his glass.

"If you accept that the effect of the white coat syndrome was non-existent in this case, for the reasons I have just outlined, then the time after the discharge of Patient A to the lunch at Blunton Lodge, was not pertinent, and therefore has no more relevance as an incident, than any of the meetings that occurred in July or August. Also, the meetings that arose in July and August, where Patient A clearly states, and the prosecution does not refute, that she had made "the worst decision of her life," clearly indicate the importance of the meeting at Blunton Lodge on Wednesday, 15th June. The reason I say this is that when one considers the time frame between the date that Patient A expressed her interest in Dr. Roseman, and the date that she informed him that she had made the worst mistake of her life, was just short of nine weeks. In which time she had enjoyed what most would believe to be an emotional high point of her life, getting married. Thus, it does seem strange for someone who, one now is being asked to believe, as a 50-year-old, was so certain of her emotions towards someone, that she married him to have had such an alteration and degeneration of her emotions some six weeks later, as to state that she had made the worst decision of her life. If her emotions were genuine, then it would not have been unreasonable for a concerned, altruistic individual to have wanted Patient A to have been certain of her emotions, before potentially making a major error of judgment. Thus, taking someone for lunch and organizing, at the last minute, a treat for someone in an attempt to allow that person to consider their position, seems a very generous and caring act to me. Now, it may not be an act that the vast majority of people would consider doing, but the fact that the majority would not be so altruistic, but more concerned about their careers and how their professional peers might judge them does not make Dr. Roseman's actions inappropriate. Foolhardy and within the cold wording of a code of conduct, unprofessional, but not unreasonable as a caring human being, which is what a profession such as chiropractic requires of its clinicians, to be able to be empathetic to their patients."

"One of the points raised, and one thing that the prosecution is stating is inappropriate, relates to the posting of images on a Facebook page. First, it should be stated categorically that Patient A contacted Dr. Roseman with a "request" to be friends on the social media site. The options are either that you accept or deny a "friend request." The proof of Patient A making the request is within the appendices of the defense bundle supplied to the Panel. It is also commented within that bundle that Dr. Roseman did not accept the "friend request" when he received it. However, when he was asked by Patient A at her next consultation if he had received it, and stated that he had, and then questioned why he did not accept it, he felt he was in a cleft stick. If he stated that he could not for professional reasons, reasons that, as a clinician herself, Patient A should have realized, then she might have been offended. So, he felt that it would be better to state that he had not got around to accepting the request, but having stated that in conversation, he realized that, subsequently, he had left himself no option but to accept the request. Dr. Roseman accepts that it was an error of judgment to "share" some of the photographs that Patient A had posted on her page and regrets that in doing so, his intent could, in hindsight, be misinterpreted. But he would state that the intent of his sharing those photos was only as a gesture of friendship, and nothing more should be read into his intent."

At that point, Malcolm Finsbury sat down and, with a cursory glance towards David, took another sip of his water.

"Thank you very much, Mr. Finsbury, for your fulsome account and submission. I feel that in part due to the depth of the deliberation that has been presented to us, we should adjourn to consider matters. I expect that it will not be pertinent for us to reconvene later on today, and therefore I would be grateful if you would both present your closing comments when we convene tomorrow at 10.00.a.m." The Chair rose as he completed his last sentence and led out the rest of the panel.

David, Malcolm, and Josephine returned to the meeting room to appraise the day. Little was stated that had not been stated numerous times before.

"Okay, now overnight, I have to write my closing remarks that I will present tomorrow morning. Is there anything particular that you feel I should stress, David?' Malcolm asked.

"Well beyond the elephant in the room in regards to the reason why Blunton Lodge happened, when it happened, as opposed to a month later, then no," David stated.

"You see, as you said in there, Dolton was clearly uncertain of her emotions prior to arriving at my clinic. I was actually only the conduit that openly caused her to question her predicament with her fiancé. The fact that I was not in a good place psychologically only compounded the issue. If she had been sure of her emotions during the period that she was a patient at my clinic, or if I had been psychologically and emotionally more stable, the events that occurred would not have happened. Now, you may feel that we cannot run with a defense that relates to my psychological state, as then I could be accused of practicing when not fit to practice. But if we did run with that defense and that somewhat exonerated my actions, what would the findings be, and what would the sanction be? Would the sanction for practicing when mentally unfit to do so be worse than what I am currently accused of, which due to the rigidity of the code of conduct, is effectively a sexual act? Also, as she was so uncertain of herself, it would have been unfair to have let her go and do something, like getting married, which she was clearly uncertain about, without facilitating her to ask herself the question. – Did she really want to marry this bloke? Thus, I think it is imperative that you connect and affiliate the lunch at Blunton Lodge to the date of flying out to Portugal rather than allow the prosecution to make a correlation between the date of discharge as a patient and the date of lunch at Blunton Lodge." David paused.

"Also, how long is too short between discharge and acceptable communication between two people, that is still deemed to be a patient-clinician situation? How long is long enough? Well, we know that from the 10th of June until the 5th of July was deemed a satisfactory period, as nothing from then on is deemed to fall within the auspices of investigation. Had Dolton been getting married in the UK and thus not flown out eight days after being discharged, allowing the Blunton Lodge meeting to have been a week later, would that have been deemed acceptable or unacceptable? So, is the issue down solely to the fact that Dolton left the country when she did? We know that 25 days was deemed acceptable, but that 5 days is deemed unacceptable. There is no specific number of days that are deemed acceptable in the code. All it says is a "reasonable period of time." So is 25 the shortest period of time that is deemed reasonable, or could it be 14 days, which, if deemed to be so, would have meant that going for lunch on 22nd June would have been acceptable? Hence as I stated before, the issue that makes my actions acceptable or unacceptable, relates solely to the fact that they were getting married abroad and hence had to travel out early to organize things, etc., and not in the UK, where they would have most probably travelled to the venue the day before. I hope you can see, Malcolm, that if the outcome of this hearing is based on a few days for the reasons given above, which were outside my control, it does seem more than a little cruel, don't you think? Also, in regards to the appropriate timeframe between discharge and social contact, doesn't her history as a clinician, in principle, enable an argument that a foreshortened time period would be appropriate in her case?" David relaxed in his chair, knowing that he had made a compelling argument.

"Okay, well, I understand where you're coming from, David, but it still is my opinion that the actions that occurred at Blunton Lodge are the damning ones and that we should not mention the timing of the wedding," Malcolm responded.

233

"But why not? It could be argued that the meet at the Bull and Baby, the telephone conversations, the meet on Burton Moor, were equally as important as the Blunton Lodge thing of themselves, or collectively, but we have been told that they occurred long enough after her discharge, not to be deemed pertinent. So, time is the main issue here, and the reason that Blunton Lodge happened when it did, was purely and simply because they were flying out to Portugal the weekend following!"

"Right, this is what I will do, I will draft my final submission overnight, and I will put that aspect of your defense in my submissions, and you can have the final say in the morning," Malcolm said in a conciliatory tone.

David accepted that proposal, but could tell that Malcolm was not happy, and David expected to perhaps revisit this conversation the next morning.

Malcolm, Josephine, and David said their fairwells for the day and headed back to their respective accommodation.

Once again, the trip back to Tom and Emily's on the ferry was a wonderful way to unwind. Although only a twenty-five-minute journey, the tranquillity of the ferry, and the views of the landmarks under floodlights, mixed with a double gin and tonic, created an appropriate full stop to the end of the day.

The five-minute walk to 11 Plainmoor Court was slightly cooler than the night before, but the weather was still very mild, particularly for November, and David felt relatively confident about the outcome the following day.

Chapter 14 – The Outcome

When David arrived at the International Dispute and Resolution Centre on Wednesday, 8th November, Malcolm was already sitting in the meeting room, writing something in his blue submission notebook.

Knowing that today would bring a resolution to the case, David had said his goodbyes to Tom and Emily earlier in the morning. They had wished him well for the outcome and asked that he ensure that he notified them of the result as soon as was practicable. He took the ferry to Blackfriars one last time and prepared himself for the outcome.

"Morning Malcolm, how are you," David said in an upbeat tone.

"Yes, good, thank you, how are you?" Malcolm responded in a caring voice.

"Good, thank you, not bad at all, to be honest," David resplied.

David realized that he was not nervous about the outcome. He had a sense that whatever the result, he would be able to deal with it without any due concerns. He was not sure why his emotions were so calm, as it was possible that he could be suspended for a few months or even removed from the register. But for some reason, he seemed content with what was to unfold.

"I have drafted my final submissions, and when Josephine arrives, I will read it through with you both, and we can then make our final decisions about it," Malcolm informed David.

David smiled within himself as he could sense that, even though Malcolm would have drafted the submission to include the timing from the Blunton Lodge lunch to the departure for Portugal, he knew

235

that there would be a final argument against its being part of his submissions.

Almost immediately, Josephine entered the room, looking somewhat flustered. She was always immaculate in her presentation, as she was again today, but for some reason, she seemed a little on edge.

"Is everything okay, Josephine?' David asked. "You do not look your usual demure, relaxed manner this morning," David asked with a degree of concern.

"Oh no, nothing, it's just that for some reason, I took the wrong bus from the hotel this morning, and it didn't come down Fleet Street but ended up going partway up Grays Inn Road before I realized my mistake. Hence the reason I am a little late, sorry." Josephine offered her apology as she took her suit jacket off and took her seat.

In the following twenty minutes, the sole issue of conversation related to whether the Blunton Lodge meeting date was highlighted. The previous arguments surfaced once again without any additional points of gravitas or relevance. However, this time, Josephine put her support directly behind Malcolm. David could not assess whether this was because Josephine honestly agreed with Malcolm or whether, as his junior effectively, she felt duty-bound to support his beliefs.

Although David felt sure that he was in the right, he stopped to consider that this was the first time that he had been in this environment, and yet both Malcolm and Josephine had been in this position multiple times before, and thus perhaps it was prudent to go with their experience, as opposed to his gut feelings.

"Okay, okay, I hear what you say, and although I do not feel that it is correct, I am paying for your professional services, and if your professional experience tells you that we should not present the time connections between Blunton Lodge and the departure for Portugal, then I will accept your advise." David realized that he had to run with the advice of experience.

Malcolm smiled, thanked David, and focused on crossing out the part of his submission that mentioned the timing connection.

At 10.12 a.m., the Court Usher called all the protagonists into the courtroom. Felicity Musselbrough and Malcolm Finsbury took approximately ten minutes each to submit their concluding remarks. The chair asked each member of the panel if they had any questions for either the prosecution or the defense, and when their responses were negative, thanked the respective barristers and informed the court that they would adjourn and consider their verdict before calling everyone back into the court to issue their decision.

The next four hours were spent discussing each other's families and the interests of their respective children, amongst a frank omission by Josephine of her love of Morris Dancing. The lack of any sense of preparation prior to informing David and Malcolm of her passion, caught the two of them so much by surprise that it was all they could do not to burst out laughing in shock and dismay of equal quarter. Fortunately, neither did laugh, but the sharp intake of breath by both of them at the same instant, followed by the unhelpful silence that ensued, whilst the two of them were attempting to compose themselves, told its own story.

At 2.07 p.m., the court usher requested all parties to return to the courtroom. Once the courtroom was assembled, and all the members of the Panel were seated, the chair read out the following Verdict, "The Professional Complaints Committee, based on the facts proven by the admission of Dr. David Roseman, the Registrant, found that the Facebook contact (during the time of the therapeutic relationship), spa day and lunch arrangement, cumulatively amounted to a course of conduct which amounted to unacceptable professional conduct."

"It considered that the spa day on its own was sufficiently serious to amount to unprofessional conduct as set out in the pertinent clause in relation to inappropriate professional behaviour."

"The Committee determined that the Registrant's behaviour had been confined to one patient only and that he had come into contact with Patient A as a direct result of his registration as a Chiropractor. The Committee did not regard it as critical that the Spa Day took place post her discharge as a patient."

"These events progressed so quickly that the Committee determined it represented a course of conduct and that it met the seriousness test. The Registrant's behaviour embraced both a risk to the reputation of the profession and also the protection of patients. Whilst the majority of the behaviour had been consensual, the Registrant had been in a position of power, he had planned the progression of the relationship, and this amounted to serious acts on his behalf".

"The PCC took into account that the incident was isolated, Dr. Roseman's previous good character, supportive references, full engagement, and partial insight. It further noted that "the Registrant had originally faced very serious allegations which he has always denied. These allegations had remained until the morning of the hearing, whereupon it was made known that Patient A's evidence could not be relied upon, or placed before the Committee and that this may have impacted on Dr. Roseman's ability to demonstrate full insight. It noted that the events had had a significant impact on Dr. Roseman personally and professionally and that at the time of the alleged events, he faced difficult personal circumstances that were no longer present. It considered that the risk of repetition was minimal. It determined that suspension would be disproportionate in all the circumstances and decided to issue the sanction of admonishment on Dr. Roseman."

"This concludes the findings, verdict, and sanction of this Professional Conduct Committee, and consequently, I close this hearing at 2.19 p.m. on Wednesday, 8th November 2017.

David sat somewhat punch drunk by the verdict of guilty but relieved at the sanction of admonishment.

Josephine, Malcolm, and David walked in silence back to the meeting room. They collected their respective files and papers, and just as David was about to say his thank you's and goodbyes, Malcolm said, "Right, anyone fancy a couple of beers? I have to stay down in town, as I have some research to do for a case starting next week, so if neither of you two have to rush off, then let me treat you to a beer or two."

David had no reason to rush back to Silkmoor as, initially, he had been told that the hearing might last the whole week. Thus he had cancelled his patients for the whole week.

"Sure, that would be great, Malcolm. Thank you. Can you come too, Josephine?"

"Most definitely, David. When did anyone of Irish decent refuse a trip to a pub?" Josephine responded with a smile.

All three burst out laughing and adjourned to the "Ye Olde Cheshire Cheese," which was almost directly across from the International Resolution and Dispute Centre and was clearly a pub that, in its day, would have been one of the beating hearts of Fleet Street, when it was the centre of journalism and most of the national newspapers.

Three beers later, and with the requisite farewells done, David walked North towards Grays Inn Road and then up to Kings Cross to catch the train up to Leeds and then onto Silkmoor.

His arrival home was unspectacular, but he allowed himself an indulgent visit to the supermarket to purchase a bottle of champagne that he would crack open later.

The following morning David contacted a friend to see if he was free to play a game of tennis. As each hour passed from the previous day, he could feel the tension of the previous sixteen months slipping away, and a new passion, to move forward in his clinic increasing, as he felt as if he was embarking on a new chapter in his career and his personal life.

David changed into his tennis kit, picked up his racquet and a new tube of balls, and was just about to leave the house when his mobile rang.

"Hello," David said, as he did whenever he answered his mobile to an unknown number.

"Hello, is that Dr. Roseman?" a polite lady's voice said on the other end of the line.

"It is. How may I help you?" David replied expectantly.

"Dr. Roseman, my name is Synthia Croyd from the Silkmoor Gazette, and I was wondering if you would like to make a comment about being found guilty of Serious Unprofessional Misconduct, please?" the lady replied.

David's heart sank. How could the local Gazette have become knowledgeable of the events that had only just occurred in London less than twenty-four hours before?

David composed himself. "I am so sorry, you have caught me just going out of the door, and I do not have time to speak with you now. Could you please give me your number? I will get back to you sometime tomorrow if that is okay?"

David took down the reporter's number, put the phone down, shrieked loudly multiple expletives, and left to play tennis.

An hour of tennis, which, with Ronen, was always an intense knock-up, as opposed to a game scenario, not only increased the heart rate and focused the mind, but allowed David to metaphorically take a breath from the receipt of the telephone call from the Silkmoor Gazette.

Ronen was an Iranian who had come over some five years earlier with his young family to hopefully attain a Ph.D. at Bradford University. His specialism was in computer technology, and it was his intent to utilise his Ph.D. to then become a tutor at Bradford University. Ronen was a very gentle man who had taken up tennis only two to three years previously, but had focused his attention on playing so much that he became very proficient in a very short period of time. David had returned to playing about eighteen months previously. He was lucky to be talented in most sports and was very able as a tennis player. However, he realised that he preferred an intense hour of knocking up with Ronen as opposed to a set or two with most others who wished to play a match. The frustration for David was that although, whilst knocking up, others went for their shots, as soon as there was a point at the end of each shot, most players played not to lose, as opposed to playing to win, and that made the game tedious.

Returning home after the game, David showered and then rang his chiropractic association to hopefully get advice in regards to what he should say or whether he should respond at all to the request for comment on the article that the Silkmoor Gazette was clearly going to run.

Twenty minutes later, David asked himself why on earth he had bothered contacting the English Chiropractic Association. The advice, which apparently came directly from Charles Taylor, was not to respond in any way.

"But what is the benefit of not responding?" David asked Melanie Sinclair, who was the ECA secretary. "We know that they are going to be writing an article, and if I am asked for a comment and do not comment, then they will probably write that *'Dr. Roseman refused to comment'* which would then allow them to imply that there was more to the situation than was being reported, and for the public to perceive that there was more to the accusation, the result being a greater issue than was actually the case!" David outlined demonstrably.

"Well, all I can say, David, is that Charles Taylor is categoric in his advise not to offer a comment," Melanie Sinclair responded in a similar tone to David.

David put the phone down to the ECA and questioned why he, and a few thousand other chiropractors, paid the thousands they did, per annum, for the poor quality of advice, the membership received.

"Is that Synthia?" David asked the woman who answered the phone.

"Yes, it is." Synthia Croyd replied.

"Could you let me have your email address Synthia so that I can pen a response to your request for a response?" David asked politely.

David wanted to write a considered response to the article that he knew would be in the Silkmoor Gazette the following Thursday. But even though he knew that it was correct to provide a response, the extent of his reply was still tempered by the negative attitude of Charles Taylor. David knew why Taylor had been so negative in relation to a response. It followed a case some six years previously when a journalist from one of the national newspapers had libelled the ECA over what he had called "bogus treatments." The ECA had taken advice and requested that the journalist retract his statement.

The journalist refused, and there then followed a ratcheting up of legal events through the court system. In the lower courts, the ECA won, but sadly, due to the massive funding behind the journalist and his insistence that this was not a simple case of misrepresentation but, in fact, to do with the British libel laws, he received support from minor celebrities, and eventually won, somehow in the High Court. The result was that the ECA had to pay the journalist damages, and costs, that financially crippled them. Consequently, all Presidents of the association that followed were very nervous about any interaction with the Press. This, therefore, would cloud their judgment in regard to anything related to the Press for a long time to come.

The next week was mild torment for David, as, on the one hand, he was able to engage with his patients once again without any need to be distracted by the ongoing professional conduct case and the worry as to whether he would be allowed to practice at its conclusion. On the other hand, he was concerned as to what the local press article would say, where in the paper it would be placed, and what the fallout from it would be.

Those seven days passed very slowly. The Silkmoor Gazette was a paper that David had delivered first thing every Thursday morning so that his patients, who had arrived early for their appointment, had something current to read.

As David walked out of the bathroom that was located at the top of the stairs on the first floor after his shower, he heard the mild thud as the Silkmoor Gazette hit the carpet underneath the letterbox of the front door of the clinic. He ran downstairs with a sense of nausea building in his stomach. After 18 months of hell that he felt he had satisfactorily negotiated eight days ago, the contents of this article could once again put his career severely at risk. He believed that the sense of relief that he had felt directly following the Hearing Outcome, and the calmness that had taken over him on the train journey home from London, was now a short-term experience.

He picked up the paper and half smiled to himself as his sensation was like a sick twist on waking up on Christmas morning as an eight-year-old. Excitement, trepidation, anxiety, and fear, all of which were similar emotions to those on 25th December, when one realised that Father Christmas had been. Excitement that he had delivered to his house, trepidation as to what the presents would be, anxiety as to whether he would get what he had hoped for, and fear that he expressed the correct emotion on realising what the present was when he opened it.

David picked up the paper and scanned the front page. He was relieved that he was not the lead story, nor was he the second story that ran along the bottom third of the paper, nor the third story that usually ran along the right-hand edge of the front page. When he had opened the clinic some 13 years previously, he had managed to get the article informing Silkmoor of the imminence of the opening of the clinic to run down the right side of the front page.

David turned inside the front cover and scanned quickly, but nothing was there. Page three, nothing. Pages four, five, and six, still nothing. He was beginning to believe that his luck had actually changed as there were many more interesting stories in and around Silkmoor that week, to need to insert his. By now, he was passing the obituaries and then into the advert pages and then the sport.

He sighed in relief and went into the kitchen to put the kettle on. In order to fill the kettle, he had to put the paper on the worktop. As he half placed and half dropped the paper, it opened on page two, and there he saw it. The article was the first column inch of the left-hand side of page two. The story covered almost the length of the page, but its location, effectively partially hidden by the thumb of anyone holding the paper, could have been a lot worse.

He read the article numerous times. The first time he felt that the reporter had been deliberately attempting to paint a picture worse than it was. The second time, he realised that the quotation that he had provided was written verbatim but would have been better if it was not so short. By the fifth time that he had read it, he believed that the article, although not a glowing endorsement of his reputation, could have been much worse than it was.

David continued to prepare for clinic and awaited the response of those patients on his list that day.

*****

Eleanor and Daniel went to a private school that was a twenty-minute train journey from Silkmoor. Part of the reason that David advocated Beachford Grammar School was due to the ease with which the children could get to school. The train journey, both to and from school, allowed them to interact with their friends before and after school. It also provided them with a sense of independence and a right of passage, travel-wise, in absolute safety.

Eleanor and Daniel had gone to Beachford at the same time. Eleanor had previously spent two years at Silkmoor Grammar. Sadly, she was the subject of bullying, and although her mother wished her to remain at Silkmoor, David was adamant that she needed a break from the bullying. Susan had also wanted Daniel to go to Silkmoor, as he had told her that he wanted to go to senior school with the friends he had made a junior school. David had felt that not having experience with other friends, Daniel would naturally have said that he wanted to go where his primary school friends were going, but that the opportunity to go to a better school, with better facilities and meet a new set of friends, was also very important. The result being that the children missed visiting and then sitting the Common Entrance exam at the same time as everyone else and had to sit a specially

n, solely for them, only nine weeks before the new
_. started.

David had actually wanted his children to go to a school that offered the opportunity of flexible boarding for his children. Like most fathers, he had wanted his children to have at least as good an education as he had had the privilege of experiencing. He had been immensely lucky to have been sent to one of the best public schools in the West Country and knew how much it had progressed him, both academically and personally. Sadly though, his ex-wife, who had not had such a privileged education, would not accommodate the children being sent to Gavelcombe Public School.

David was aware that due to the unfortunate narcissistic trait of his ex-wife and her desire to have her children close at hand, she would never tolerate sending them to a better school, for fear of not seeing them on a daily basis.

Regrettably, such a decision, and the reasons behind it, and the consequent negative effect on his children, that therefore ensured that David's children went to Beachford Grammar School, would not become manifest for many years, and sadly to the great detriment of Daniel, and his long term life prospects.

On the Monday following the publishing of the article in the Silkmoor Gazette, Eleanor and Daniel arrived in Silkmoor on the 4.55 p.m. train from Beachford. Even in the short time that they had been at Beachford, they travelled in separate carriages, as each of them had separate friendship groups.

As Susan lived only five minutes walk from the station, the children usually walked home. Their walk took them passed David's clinic, so they would always drop in to say hello.

On this Monday, Eleanor decided that she would pop into the supermarket, whose car park abutted the exit from the station, to get

246

some sweets to eat whilst she was doing her homework. She walked across the car park and into the supermarket, and to the aisle dedicated to confectionery. Once she had chosen what she wanted, she paid at the self-service counter and started to leave the shop. Beside the exit to the shop was a newspaper kiosk.

"Eleanor, Eleanor, how are you?" said a voice from the kiosk.

Eleanor turned and noticed Grace smiling at her as she walked purposefully to chat with Eleanor. Eleanor had got to know Grace in the two years that she was at Silkmoor Grammar School.

"So, how is Beachford Grammar?" Grace asked.

"Oh, it's wonderful," Eleanor said with a smile.

"How are things at Silkmoor? " Eleanor asked, mostly to be polite rather than with real interest, as she was delighted to have moved on and had no desire to be told anything about the school.

"Oh fine, really, nothing is any different," Grace said forlornly. "Listen, what's this about your Dad?" Grace asked excitedly and inquisitively.

"What about my Dad?" Eleanor asked, concerned and questioningly.

"Have you not seen this week's Silkmoor Gazette?" Grace asked with surprise.

"No, no, no, I haven't," Eleanor responded.

"Well, he's been found guilty of unprofessional conduct. Apparently, he kissed one of his patients." Grace happily explained.

Eleanor stood motionless, said her goodbyes to Grace, and returned to the kiosk to buy the Gazette.

Eleanor walked purposefully home, straight passed her father's clinic, which, as it was winter, allowed her to look into the reception area through the large window that fronted onto the street. Her father was sitting at the computer at the rear of the Reception, but as the computer was on a table on the side wall, he was looking perpendicular to the angle of view of Eleanor. She half stopped, considering going in and confronting him, but decided to hurry home so that she could read the article.

She entered her mother's house through the French windows at the back of the property, gave her Mum a quick kiss, and made her excuses to go up to her bedroom.

Once in her bedroom, Eleanor flicked hurriedly through the paper, desperately looking for the article about her Dad.

During the investigations, David had chosen not to mention it to the children. He had mentioned it in passing to Susan and had even asked her for a character reference to assist his defence for the Fitness to Practice Hearing in November 2016. But when she refused to respond to his requests, he chose to keep the whole matter to himself. At that moment he had realised that even in a professional capacity, this woman was not going to lift a finger to assist him, even though she had worked with him very happily professionally for nine years.

Once the Hearing was over, he had considered mentioning it to Eleanor and Daniel at some stage when they were a fair degree older. Once he knew that the article would appear in the Gazette, he was uncertain whether he should tell them or not. On reflection, he had decided that, as it was not a paper that was usually read by children, there was no need to tell them what had happened. Of course, he did not consider the possibility of a school friend whose parents had read the article mentioning it to their daughter, who then just happened to bump into Eleanor a few days later.

Once Eleanor had read the article, she decided to investigate the matter further. Eleanor was a very studious girl who, like her Dad, was very iconoclastic and also inquisitive. She accessed the General Chiropractic Council website and found the page of complaints raised.

For the next fifteen minutes, she read all the accusations that Jenny Dolton had raised during her initial submission of statements. For some inexplicable reason, despite the fact that Dolton had been designated to be an unreliable witness, and none of her accusations had been deemed creditable to be presented to the Hearing, each and every accusation was still available to be accessed on the CBUK website. The Policy of the CBUK was that all matters appertaining to a case would be readily available on their website for 12 months following the conclusion of any investigation or hearing.

Eleanor, who had spent the four years since the divorce of her parents almost totally in the company of her mother, had thus grown up with a very negative perception of her father. This perception had been created by either the negative commentary that she would have received from her mother or, if more passively, due to the lack of time spent with her father during these formative years. Eleanor was 8 when her parents split up and initially took it out on her mother. However, over time, she became more and more resentful of her father. In truth, she did not know why she had become more resentful of her father, and pragmatically, there was no logical reason why she should have done. After all, however, unfortunate the emotional effect of divorce was for the children of the family, the resultant live style change should allow the children to end up with two separate families and two separate homes that they share equally with the respective parents. The fact that David and Susan's respective houses were only two hundred and fifty yards apart should have meant that, for the most part, the children could have enjoyed the company of both of their parents equally.

David had, on numerous occasions, attempted to communicate with his daughter, but she had chosen not to respond, or when she did, to respond in a very angry and defamatory manner. David had regularly told Susan that the lack of time spent with each parent would be extremely detrimental to the children in the short term and, maybe, the long term also. However, Susan, for some unexplainable reason, had chosen never to discipline either child or to provide parental advice. She had decided that they would make their own decisions in regard to whether they saw their father or not. The fact that the decisions would be made on an emotional and often irrational scale based on the defamatory information provided to them by their mother, did not seem to bother Susan, which David always found to be particularly ironic.

Susan had, throughout her teenage years and well into her twenties, never wished for children and never saw herself as a mother. It was only after she had met David that she acquired any maternal emotions. There were a number of occasions where they had been in the company of a friend's young children, where Susan had no concept of how to deal with the needs of a child. However, irrespective of the rancour during and following their divorce, David would always espouse how amazing Susan had been during both pregnancies and in the weaning of Eleanor and Daniel.

The resultant emotion within Eleanor from reading the accusations, embroiled with her embedded disregard and disrespect for her father, was an aggressive, resentful, and inherent embarrassment. How could what she allowed herself to perceive as this hateful and shameful man actually be her father? How could such a man cause her such embarrassment in front of an old school friend? Who did he think he was that he had not told her that the article was about to be published, and when did he not think about her emotions? She was seething, but, on reflection, because of the image that she had allowed to develop in her head of her father over the years, she was not at all surprised. Eleanor displayed all the immature emotions anu parent would expect a child of that age to display.

"Why the fuck did you not tell me that this article was going to appear in the Silkmoor Gazette, David?" Eleanor said in her text to her father shortly after completing the reading of the article.

Eleanor knew how unhappy David was to be called by his Christian name by her. So, whenever she wished to show dissension, she chose not to call him "Dad."

"Hi Eleanor, it would be much better and more appropriate if you came up this evening so that I could talk to you about what has been going on. I am free all night; just let me know when you're free to come up," David responded in a calm manner.

"I don't want to speak to you about it, "kissing a patient!" that's disgusting, and you should be ashamed of yourself. You should have been struck off!" Eleanor texted in return, her aggression and anger very explicit.

"As I have said in my last text Eleanor, please come up and talk to me, and I will explain everything that happened. You will not comprehend the truth of the events that happened from a short newspaper article, or from looking at the various things posted on the CBUK website," David replied calmly once again.

"The truth is very clear, you fucking idiot. I do not want to talk to you and hear your lies. Leave me alone!" Eleanor responded.

"Eleanor, you do not know any details of the story. You have read what you have read and made a snap decision. Respectfully, that is not what people within families do. At the very least, those within families should talk and listen to each other, before making judgments about a member of their family. If I had made a judgment about you, based on what my mother told me about your friend and the drugs that she took when she was with you, and the involvement of the Police,

ion of you would have been a lot different. It is extremely
... to rash conclusions about somebody, particularly when
one does not have all the facts and also when one wants to paint
someone in a bad light. I am not going to go into any more detail here
by text. Please come up and see me, and then we can talk through
exactly what happened, and then you can make your own valued
judgments." David responded.

"Fuck off, David, it is clear what and who you are, and I do not
want anything more to do with you!" Eleanor signed off aggressively.

David penned another short text but realised, as he attempted to
send it, that his daughter had blocked her phone from receiving his
messages.

David sat quietly on the sofa, contemplating the last four years
and wondering why he seemed to be constantly the butt of misfortune
and negativity. He had spoken to a number of friends, in recent years,
about the unpleasant manner that his daughter had treated him.
Almost without exception, particularly when talking with women, the
response had been, "Well, it's a difficult age for a girl. Her hormones
are all over the place. Not to worry, she will grow out of it." No one
felt that it was inappropriate to let girls just be insensitive, belligerent,
and downright nasty to their fathers. No one thought that the lack of
discipline throughout their teenage years and allowing girls to get
away with their awful attitude and behaviour might actually be
condoning them to act in that manner throughout their adult life.
Interestingly, boys, who also obviously went through their own
puberty, were never given the same latitude as girls. Why was that,
David wondered.

Sadly, he was not as circumspect about the probability of his
daughter "getting over things in time." He believed that the lack of
time spent in those years, between eight to fourteen or fifteen, would
result in there actually never being the bond that there should have

been between a father and his daughter. But having beaten himself up many, many times in attempting to find a way through the morass of lack of communication, he had resigned himself to the status that Gordon Fenton had advised during one of their many conversations at the bar in The Bulls Head. "You can only play the cards that you have been dealt, David. Even though you should have been dealt better cards, that would have allowed you to do more of what you know that you should be doing as a father, you can only play the cards that you have been dealt, mate. So all you can do is make sure that you play the cards that you have been dealt in the best way that you can."

David considered how on earth a woman like Susan could call herself a decent mother, when she had not only chosen not to consider the wellbeing and happiness of the children when she unilaterally chose to divorce David. But thereafter, even though she had devastated everyone else's life in the family, to suit her selfish desires, she did not have the decency to realise the importance of supporting the children to have a meaningful relationship with their father, who she knew to be immensely caring, considerate and dedicated to his children.

David poured himself a large gin and sighed as he realised how much his daughter was missing out on, and the sadness of her unwarranted negativity towards him.

The following day, Daniel arrived off the train from school and came to David's for his dinner as it was a Thursday. During the divorce settlement, it had been agreed that the children would spend every other weekend with David and every Monday and Thursday night with him. However, due to the fact that Susan wanted to extract more money from him, from the Child Maintenance Service, she forced the children to return to her house every Monday and Thursday to ensure that they slept under her roof. The CMS had a very simplistic calculation of money provided by the father based on where the children slept. The fact that the cost of cooking a meal and other food that the children ate whilst at the father's house was much greater than the nominal cost of sleeping in a bed, did not register with the CMS.

*****

David felt that his Friday morning clinic, directly after the publications of the article in the press might be interesting. Would there be cancellations, or would there be comments from patients? Should he raise the issue?

On reflection, he felt that he would be succinct with his responses to all patients. He would not start the conversation. It was important to inform patients that the witness who had complained had been deemed to be unreliable and thus had been proven to have lied throughout her witness statements. David would also remind patients that he had been admonished and, therefore, despite everything that had been presented, his governing body had decided that beyond a cursory slap on the wrists, there was no requirement to sanction him further or to direct that he retrained, in any shape or form. Thus, the only conclusion that one should draw from the hearing was that the panel had decided that there was no risk at all to the general public and that David was fit to resume his practice forthwith.

Martin Bainbridge was David's first patient at 7.20 on Friday morning.

"Morning Martin, how was your weekend?" David asked in a very upbeat manner.

"Good, thank you, David, and yours?" Martin asked in a slightly refrained manner.

"Very good thank you. My son was over, and we played some table tennis and went to the cinema. How's your low back feeling? Percentage-wise, how much better are you feeling than just on Tuesday? David asked in a politely concerned manner.

"Well, my level of pain has reduced from about a 6 out of 10 to a 4. So, I am able to move about more without the twinges in my lumbar region," Martin responded positively.

"Excellent," David replied as Martin lay face down on the bench, and David started to administer some soft tissue work to Martin's low lumbar spine.

The two conversed for a while about Martin's passion, which was golf. Martin was a member of a course about five miles from Silkmoor, which was renowned for the steepness of its two finishing holes, such that, locally, they were called the cardiac climb. Many people regularly joked that there should be a mobile defibrillator beside the eighteenth tee box.

"I saw the article about your case in the Gazette this morning," Martin said after a slight pause in the conversation.

"Oh, okay," David responded meekly. Martin was not one of the patients whom David had asked for a letter of support, as he was a relatively new patient, and their relationship was solely a patient-clinician relationship.

"My wife read the article and said that I should cancel my appointment," Martin said quite forcibly. "But I told her that if one read between the lines, you could see that there was something not quite right with the woman who had made the complaint," Martin said in a reassuring manner.

"Well, as you can imagine, it would not be professional to discuss the case, but all I can say is that the complaint was investigated in great detail and that although I was deemed to have breached the Code of Conduct by the strict letter of the Code, I did not do anything that any other small businessman would not have done in similar circumstances. It is only that in my profession, the concept of being a clinician, as well as being in business, is not something that my governing body appreciates. But they were conclusive and unanimous that my sanction was only to be an admonishment, and therefore, that speaks for itself. But thank you for being open about your opinion Martin. That's very reassuring." David said warmly.

The rest of David's day went off without any concerns or cancellations. Some patients, particularly the ones who knew him well, proactively raised the article and were effusive in their support for his predicament. All those that mentioned the case said how sorry they were that David had had to go through the stress of the investigation and they were delighted that he had come out of the other end relatively unscathed.

David returned to his regular tennis sessions, and little, if anything, was mentioned by any of his friends from that day forward. The one thing that David could not rationalise was how the Silkmoor Gazette got hold of the story. The only conclusion that David came to was that the Gazette used the keyword "Silkmoor" in a number of its search engines in an attempt to be notified of any news stories that may be in the public interest of its catchment readership. Thus, his clinic, named after the town in which he worked, might have triggered the search engine notification. Frustrating beyond belief, but due to his lack of good fortune in recent years, not something about which David was at all surprised.

The remainder of the year before Christmas was relatively uneventful. David had chosen to start his Christmas shopping at the beginning of December this year, as opposed to what had been his habit since his early twenties of leaving all his shopping until Christmas Eve. He hoped that thinking and acting in a seasonal manner a few weeks earlier than normal this year would allow him to enjoy the Christmas break that much more.

Chapter 15 – Authority Incompetence

The twenty-two months following his Professional Conduct Hearing were generally uneventful for David Roseman. Regrettably, the article posted in the Silkmoor Gazette did have a negative effect, that it would not have done had it been published fifteen years before.

Before the advent of the internet, it was always said that today's news stories were tomorrow's chip wrappers. Thus, if one could weather that initial storm, things would wash over, and in a relatively short period of time, things would go back to normal.

Sadly, with the advent of the internet, yesterday's news was readily available online, ad infinitum. Due to the fact that David's practice was named after the town in which he worked, which, as the first chiropractor in the town, seemed a reasonable decision at the time - whenever anyone looked on a search engine for a "chiropractor in Silkmoor" the article which was tagged to "Silkmoor" and "chiropractor" would always appear towards the top of the first page of the search engine.

David calculated that he had probably lost in excess of £20,000 per annum due to the presence of the article. But having spoken to the editor of the Gazette, who, although superficially seemed helpful, then refused to remove the article, even though he knew that it was detrimental to David's practice, based on the spurious argument that it was "archive" material.

In a lengthy and somewhat heated exchange with Paul Mason, the editor of the Silkmoor Gazette, David informed him that if someone wished to research articles or practitioners who had been accused of misconduct and, in putting the appropriate key words into a search engine, came up with the article, that would be fair and reasonable. However, for those people who put in the keywords "back pain" or "chiropractor in Silkmoor," to then have access to the article was incorrect, inappropriate and deliberately detrimental to the sustainability of David's business.

The conclusion of the telephone conversation with Paul Mason only reinforced David's longstanding belief that journalists are not people who are interested in the wellbeing of those that they write about. They are only interested in selling newspapers and have little or no care for the consequences of their articles.

In the intervening two years, David had been able to improve his relations with Eleanor, such that in 2018 she joined David and Daniel on both a skiing holiday in March to the French Alps and a summer holiday to Crete in early July. One of the benefits of sending children to a private school was that they finished their academic year earlier than the state schools, and therefore the cost of flights to sunnier climbs was always slightly cheaper than in the height of the summer holiday season.

On 30th October 2019, at approximately 10.15 am., in the morning, there was a knock on the clinic entrance door. Luckily David did not have a patient at that time as it was a Wednesday and thus his day off.

The postman handed David his post and then informed him that there was a letter to sign for. Due to the numerous letters that David had had to sign during the 18 months of the professional conduct investigations, whenever there was a letter to sign, his heart sank.

Wednesday, October 30th 2019, produced the same sinking feeling as had been present three years previously.

"Sorry mate, just got a letter for you to sign for there," the postman said in a mildly embarrassed manner, almost as if he had known from whom the letter had been sent.

David signed the postman's tablet and took the envelope into his office.

He recognized the postmark instantly. Perplexed and slightly agitated, he opened the envelope. The letter was headed The General Chiropractic Council.

The letter read:-

Dear Dr. Roseman,

Re: Update

We write to inform you that following notification of the receipt of a complaint against you, we have requested a formal witness statement from the complainant.

Once we are in receipt that witness statement, we will notify you formally of the complaint.

Yours sincerely

Katie Williams

Fitness to Practice Officer

Having read the letter, David was more than perplexed. What was this an update of? To what did it relate?

Luckily as October 30th was a Wednesday, David could focus on attempting to get to the bottom of the letter. He rang the main number of the CBUK and chose the appropriate selection from the voice recording.

"Hello, CBUK Julie Bignal speaking, how can I help you?"

"Good morning Julie. My name is Dr. David Roseman. I am in receipt of a letter from Katie Williams regarding a prospective complaint. Could I speak with her, please?" David asked politely.

"I am afraid that she is away from her desk at the moment. Can I ask you to call back later, please?" Julie Bignal replied.

"Well, as I am not aware of how long Katie might be away from her desk, may I ask you to ask her to give me a call when she returns, please, and can you tell her that it is quite urgent?" David said is a firm tone.

"Oh, okay, yes, certainly. What's your number, please?" Julie asked.

David gave his number and put the phone down. He presumed that as Katie Williams was "away from her desk", it would not be that long before he heard back from her. Sadly, even though he called the CBUK in the mid-morning, he did not receive a call back that morning.

When he rang again in the mid-afternoon, David was informed that she was still away from her desk but was assured that she would ring him back once she returned.

No call was received by the end of 30th October.

Following his flourish of early morning patients the next day, David called the CBUK to speak with Katie Williams.

"Hello CBUK, Julie Bignal speaking, how may I help you?"

"Hi Julie, it's Dr. Roseman here again, I rang yesterday to speak with Katie Williams, but sadly she did not call me back. Can you put me through to her, please?" David asked politely.

"Oh, I am so sorry. Katie is on annual leave now for a few days and won't be back until next Tuesday. Would you mind calling again then?" Julie replied in a very matter-of-fact manner, totally oblivious to the urgency of the call received the previous day.

"Sorry, Julie, it was urgent that I spoke with Katie yesterday, and respectfully I cannot wait until sometime next week. I have received a confusing letter from Katie that I need information and clarification on as soon as possible. May I please speak with Katie's line manager?" David said, clearly getting somewhat agitated now.

The line went quiet for a short while as David waited tentatively.

"Good morning Dr. Roseman. My name is Michael Fisher. I am Katie's line manager. I understand that you have received a letter from her and that you need some clarification. How can I help?" Michael Fisher said in an authoritative but kind voice.

"First, thank you for taking my call Michael. The issue is that I received a letter, recorded delivery yesterday, stating that it was "updating" me on the status of a complaint, and as yet, I am unaware of the existence of any notification of a complaint and so cannot comprehend their being an update." David explained as calmly as he felt able to.

Since its inception, the CBUK had been a very tortuous organization to deal with. Most of the problems that emanated from the CBUK seemed to be based around the total incompetence and lack of intellect of those officers who worked there. Thus, no-one was ever at all desirous of engaging with it as a governing body for fear of saying something that was perceived incorrectly and thus misconstrued inappropriately.

"You were sent an initial letter on 1st October, but I see here that there is no notification as to whether you received the letter." Michael Fisher observed.

"Well, I can assure you that I did not receive any letter previously. I presume that it too would have been sent, by registered post, would it?" David asked, mildly frustrated.

"Yes, it would have done, and it clearly was, but as I have just said, there is no commentary that states that you have received it. So I imagine that it was sent back to us, but we did not make a record of that fact. Therefore, I must apologise Dr. Roseman".

But I can tell you that the letter sent out on 1st October related to the complaint that was investigated back in 2017." Michael Fisher explained.

"Sorry, I do not understand. How can it relate to the complaint that was tabled, investigated and adjudicated between the Autumn of 2016 and late 2017? That matter must be closed now, surely? Neither party to the complaint process, neither plaintiff nor defendant appealed the decision of the Professional Conduct Panel at the time, and thus surely that must be the end of it." David fluctuated from being perplexed to being angry that his governing body could once again embroil him in matters that had been concluded over two years before.

"I am very sorry, Dr. Roseman, I can understand your frustration, but I cannot give you any more information now beyond what I can see on file as it relates to the receipt of his complaint", Michael tried to be helpful.

Can you at least tell me what the nature of the current complaint is, please?' David asked.

"Let me send you the first letter that you should have received by email now so that you can read it and comprehend the nature of the current situation, and if you have any queries, please feel free to get back to us." Michael Fisher said, again in a mildly concerned manner.

David read the complaint letter that was sent from the husband of Jenny Dolton / Rossington.

On further investigation, the letter revisited every accusation made back in 2016, each of which was clearly stated by the Investigating Committee at the time as being false and unreliable.

The one thing that the letter informed David of, that he was not aware of until this notification, was that Simon Rossington was now a divorcee again.

In his letter, he stated that the reason for his divorce was solely due to the events that occurred back in the Spring of 2016. The fact that Jenny Dolton, as she was at the time, was not even married during the period of time that she was a patient at Silkmoor clinic, let alone a patient once she was married, did not seem to be something that Simon Rossington could compute.

Reading between the lines, it was clear that Rossington wanted someone to blame for his second marriage failure and perhaps wanted to gain some compensation from David, if he could prove that his marriage had broken up as a result of the consultations that his now ex-wife had had in May and early June of 2016.

Once he had read the letter of complaint, David relaxed as he realized that there was nothing new in the complaint. Rossington had not even been a patient, so how on earth could he be aggrieved? The one concern that David had related to why the CBUK had countenanced any communication from Rossington, let alone requesting a formal witness statement from him.

David decided to write to the Registrar of the CBUK, Russell Anlaby, who had only recently become the new registrar.

Receiving an expeditious and considered response from Russell Anlaby, it was clear that he was someone with whom one could engage in a reasoned conversation. From the emails that flowed between the Registrar and David, it was clear that there was a flaw in the manner by which the original clauses of The Chiropractic Act had been drafted. The original act had not made any provision for triaging any complaint. Each and every complaint had to be fully assessed, and witness statements requested, from both the plaintiff and the defendant, so that the Investigating Committee could assess the validity of the complaint received.

Thus, even though everyone knew that the complaint received from Simon Rossington was exactly the same as the complaint received in late 2016, for which everyone knew of the outcome, they did not have the vehicle to legally dismiss the complaint.

David communicated with the Registrar to inform him that the Investigating Committee had no choice but to discard the current complaint. Because if they took any credence from it, in any way and thus chose to investigate further, the action of doing so would not only totally undermine the trust of any chiropractor in their professional conduct procedures and protocol in the future. But as importantly, it would critically undermine the findings of the previous professional conduct panel, who had dutifully sat and considered this very same information some years previously.

Despite this very clear and definitive observation made by David, the CBUK notified him that it had to comply with its various terms and conditions, as outlined within the statute that provided them with its authority.

Consequently, over the following ten few weeks, David had to respond to the statements made by Rossington via his solicitors to the exact same accusations that had been tabled, verbatim, three years earlier.

Fortuitously, in both time spent and emotional energy expended, David was able to reply to each accusation with the same response – "This accusation has already been considered previously".

After the necessary timeframe of batting back statements and counter statements, the complaint was presented to the Investigating Committee, who, on the 6th of November 2019, exactly two years to the day after the Fitness to Practice Hearing, issued a directive that "We The Investigating Committee, having considered all the evidence placed before us, content that there is No Case to Answer, in relation to the accusations tabled by Mr. Simon Rossington on 2nd. September 2019."

*****

It is now seven years since Jenny Dolton and her aggressive and extremely unpleasant husband tabled a complaint about David Roseman.

In March 2020, Susan, David's ex-wife, tabled a complaint about David to the CBUK based on vexatious and false hearsay and accusations. Again, after the necessary statements and counter statements, the Investigating Committee once again found no case to answer.

Leading up to Christmas 2019, both Peter and Andrew Butterfield, a father and son who had been regular patients of David's for many years, reminded him of their invite to join them on the evening of Builder's Friday at the Snipe and Bucket pub as part of their Christmas celebrations.

Builder's Friday was not something that David had come across when he lived down South, even when he worked as an architect. He had only experienced its existence when he moved to Yorkshire. So he was unsure if it was only a Yorkshire thing or a Northern thing. Simply put, on the last Friday before Christmas, most of those who worked in, and associated with the construction industry, would take the Friday afternoon off and head to a local pub to enable them to slowly glide into Christmas.

This father and son tarmacking company, who had plied their trade in the Silkmoor area for in excess of 40 years, invited a number of friends and associates each year to join them at the Snipe and Bucket, to send off packing the work year that they had just completed. David had been invited the year previously, but as he had Daniel staying that weekend, he could not take up the invite.

On this particular evening, he had had a couple of his last patients before Christmas cancel, which meant that he finished early and decided to catch the train to Gulmley and join them in the pub.

Unsurprisingly, a wonderful evening was had by all, and as most of the guests were heading off, Peter and his brother John asked David if he wished to share a taxi home with them to Silkmoor. David readily agreed, and four of them duly crammed into the back of the taxi.

On the journey home, Peter asked David if he had ever been into one of the smallest pubs in Burton-on-Aire, the Rats Hole. David confirmed that he knew where the pub was, but that he had never ventured inside, but would be happy to drop in on the way home. The brothers laughed profusely as they suggested that David walk in alone and see what reaction he got from the locals.

Being up for a laugh, when the taxi dropped them all off outside the Rats Hole, David dutifully walked into the pub alone. A re-enaction of the opening scene to American Werewolf in London could not have been better staged than what occurred when David walked into the Rats Hole.

The pub, which only had enough standing room for thirty people, went from the normal noisy hubbub of a pub on a Friday night, to the quietness one only hears when a coffin is lowered into a grave by the

267

pallbearers, instantly. A few seconds later, having allowed the full effect of the silence to play out, the remainder of the party came into the pub laughing.

Once they had placed their orders at the bar and had pints in hand, David looked around the pub, and with the same speed that the bar had gone silent when he walked him, his jovial emotional frivolity exited him in an instant, when his eyes crossed a stocky, black-haired man's eyes in the corner of the pub. Simon Rossington had his eyes fixed onto David's with a glare that appeared almost demonic.

After a short while, Rossington turned to someone on his left and engaged in fervent conversation, regularly turning to stare back at David whilst continuing in conversation. The pair where stood beside the jukebox.

Immediately after Rossington stopped talking, he left the bar.

On the drive over, Peter had mentioned the jukebox and how many great old tunes they had on it. Having seen the jukebox beside Rossington, David decided to go and have a look at what was on it, once Rossington had left the pub. In doing so, David came into close proximity to the gentleman that Rossington had been talking to before he had left.

"What's your name mate?" Rossington's acquaintance asked David.

"Sorry?" David replied.

What's your name, mate? It's a simple fucking question, "the acquaintance asked once more, tension filling the air.

"Sorry, why would you want to know my name?" David asked again.

"Well, I don't really, but I think I should give you some advice," the man said.

"Oh, okay, so what's the advice?" David asked somewhat tentatively.

"Well, you see that bloke I was chatting to before he left. Well, he's a bit of a nutter, alright, but he says that you ruined his marriage, and he has gone outside to ring up his brothers, to get them to come over here and do you in. So, if I was you, I would leave this pub now, before he comes back because he isn't very happy!" the man said forcibly.

"Oh, okay, well, thank you for the advice, but I am here with some friends, celebrating Christmas and have no intention of leaving until we are ready to leave," David informed the gentleman firmly.

"Well, that's up to you, mate, but he said that he thought he would be able to ruin your career by notifying the Silkmoor Gazette about your professional conduct hearing, but understands that you're still practicing. So, seeing you here now, he intends to make sure that he ruins you. I know he's a nutter, and he is off his head, but he has some very unpleasant connections in Kelbrook, who you do not want to meet. He comes from a very rough family. Two of his brothers have done time for GBH, and I would not be surprised if they would happily do it again if he was to ask them. So be warned, just be warned," the man said eerily.

David returned to Peter and John having put "Band on The Run" by Wings on the Jukebox, which he thought was apt, having heard that those who may be coming for him had already been in prison!

Finishing his pint shortly afterwards, David wished his friends a Merry Christmas, ordered a taxi and made his way home, contemplating.

Well, if nothing else, he thought, this evening had answered the conundrum regarding how "The Silkmoor Gazette" had been fed the information about his hearing outcome so rapidly. Clearly, the CBUK

269

notified Jenny directly following the end of the hearing, and Rossington, whose sole aim had been to get David struck off in the first place , being annoyed and frustrated that the CBUK had not done his bidding, had decided to take matters into his own hands and contacted the newspaper with the appropriate link.

Who would have thought that, at the time of choosing to retrain for five years in a field of medicine that is predicated on helping others to remove their pain and biomechanical suffering, one of the needless and most hurtful consequences would be to be subjected to repeated, unpleasant and needless accusations as regards the integrity and honest intent of an altruistic and caring individual, just trying to be there to help? And had the professional hearing brought to an end this unpleasant matter? At the end of the hearing, David had naturally thought it had, but from the unseemly events in the Rats Hole that night, who could say!

Ingram Content Group UK Ltd.
Milton Keynes UK
UKHW021824190723
425448UK00010B/516

9 781916 540767